WHO WAS ADAM?

In the continual debate on "Genesis 1 and 2 – Myth, poetry or fact?" – the science of prehistoric anthropology has been overlooked. Yet might not the Bible all along have held the answers to many enigmas of pre-history? Victor Pearce argues that it is time to stop discussing out-dated theories and to take a fresh look at the Genesis problem in the light of modern scientific discovery. As an anthropologist he shows that the story of Adam and his Garden fills vital gaps in our knowledge of New Stone Age Man and his origins. He also examines recent biological research into the origin of life and discusses these findings in the light of the Christian teaching of a Creator God.

The whole approach is both original and scientific; the author determinedly faces both the problems and the implications of scientific discoveries. *Who was Adam?* should provide a talking-point for thoughtful readers for many years to come.

Titles in this Series

WHO WAS ADAM?

by

E. K. VICTOR PEARCE

B.Sc. (Hons. Anthropology, Lond.), Dip. Anth. (Oxon.), A.L.C.D., F.R.A.I., C.F.
Prebendary of Lichfield Cathedral

EXETER:
THE PATERNOSTER PRESS LTD

AUSTRALIA:
Emu Book Agencies Pty., Ltd.,
63 Berry Street, Granville 2142 N.S.W.

SOUTH AFRICA:
Oxford University Press
P.O. Box 1141, Oxford House, 11, Buitencingle St.,
Cape Town

Made and printed in Great Britain for
The Paternoster Press, Paternoster House,
3 Mount Radford Crescent, Exeter, Devon
by Butler & Tanner Ltd,
Frome and London

CONTENTS

CONTENTS

ILLUSTRATIONS

ACKNOWLEDGEMENTS: Figs. 1, 12 and 14 are from S. Cole, *The Neolithic Revolution*, and Figs. 4, 5, 6 and 15 are from Kenneth P. Oakley, *Man the Toolmaker*, both by permission of the British Museum (Natural History). Fig. 2 is from the Yale Babylonian Collection, by permission; Figs. 8 and 9 are from *The Scientific American* by permission of W. H. Freeman & Co.; Fig. 10 is from J. Mellaart, *Catal Hüyük*, by permission of the author and Thames and Hudson; Fig. 16 is from

J. D. Watson, *The Biology of the Gene*, by permission of W. A. Benjamin, Inc.; Fig. 17 is from G. Chedd, *What is Life?*, B.B.C. T.V. Publication. The Author and Publishers acknowledge these permissions with thanks. Original drawings, Figs. 2, 3, 11, 13, 16, 19, 20, are by the Author.

PREFACE

DEVELOPMENTS IN SCIENTIFIC DISCOVERY HAVE BEEN SO RAPID THAT WE are now able to see an exciting connection between the Bible and science in two fields of investigation. In the field of anthropology, the identification of Adam with New Stone Age man by the use of proper diagnostic principles, is now becoming apparent. Before this clue, Christian writers on science seemed to be rather in the dark where a biblical application of anthropology was concerned. In the field of genetics, the knowledge of the complex cell-mechanism shared by man and beast, makes the materialist speculations on life's origin increasingly inadequate. Moreover, the discoveries about the DNA genetic code heighten the significance of God's speech in creation and of the Word made flesh at the Incarnation.

Many helpful apologetics have been written by scientists qualified in disciplines such as physics, chemistry, and biology. They have made valuable contributions to Christian knowledge, demonstrating the reasonableness of faith in the Creator, but because the Bible is largely a book on anthropology (and of course theology), scholars not qualified in this particular discipline have found it necessary to investigate it. Anthropology is, however, a very specialized subject, and without training it is possible to lose one's way.

Anthropology is the Science of Man, which makes it a comprehensive discipline. It has three main subsections: Physical Anthropology, Prehistoric Archaeology, and Social Anthropology. These include genetics, anatomy, the study of fossils, geology, zoology of the primates, and the study of present primitive races throughout the world with their beliefs, social structures, economy and technology. It makes a fascinating subject, especially when it highlights the truths and background of the Bible. Every theologian ought to be an anthropologist!

Some of the material in this book has developed from a paper which was read to the SCM Science Group at Oxford, and later to the Research Scientists' Christian Fellowship of Southampton University.

I wish to record my indebtedness to some of the great names in anthropology and archaeology, both at Oxford and London Universities. I am particularly grateful to Professors Seton Lloyd and James Mellaart for their personal guidance. Also to Prof. E. E. Evans-Pritchard, the acknowledged pioneer of a more accurate approach to social anthropology, and to Dr. K. Burridge and others in Pitt-Rivers Museum,

Oxford. In the rather specialized realm of pleistocene geology, Mr. Baden-Powell of Oxford, a nephew of the founder of the Scout Movement, was of great help in seeking out clues. I am grateful to Prof. Daryll Forde for making available the facilities of his departments at University College London.

For many theologians who are showing interest in anthropology through the works of Teilhard de Chardin, I have endeavoured to show the limitation he suffered because of the position of science at the time of his writing, without detracting from his positive contributions.

It is hoped that qualified anthropologists will forgive my use of non-technical terms where possible in the interests of the general reader. I have endeavoured to keep close to facts, many of which have come firsthand from those mentioned above, but of course there is a margin for interpretation in many matters.

The last five chapters of the book have been added because of the growing interest in life's origins, and the discoveries of the unity of all life as seen in the cellular and subcellular organizations of our bodies. Without a consideration of the origin of Adam's cells the picture would not be complete, and indeed this may prove eventually to be the most important section of the book.

Some without training in the sciences may feel that there is a simple answer to some questions considered here. It would be appreciated if they could exercise patience for the sake of students who have to investigate problems by the use of the scientific method and for whom this work may well be of help.

September, 1970   E. K. VICTOR PEARCE

PREFACE TO THE SECOND EDITION

I T IS GRATIFYING THAT THE BOOK HAS BEEN SO WIDELY REVIEWED. Further discoveries on American origins appear on p. 59f. Discussion has arisen on both sides of the Atlantic on whether there were two Adams. The word *adam* is a generic noun and merely means "man" and in Genesis 1 is so used. But from chapter 2 onwards Adam refers to an individual. Thus only one Adam was ancestor to this present world population (cf. p. 21). All races now inhabiting the earth are descended from one comparatively recent Homo sapiens stock. All earlier types of man have died out (p. 14).

As this work covers so wide a field, I am indebted to scholars who have checked its accuracy where it comes within their own sphere.

March, 1974   E. K. VICTOR PEARCE

CHAPTER I

ABANDONED THEORIES

W E HAVE REACHED A POINT IN THE DIALOGUE BETWEEN SCIENCE AND Biblical theology when we can take stock of the situation, especially as it relates to the problem of early man. New vistas of knowledge on both sides impel a reshuffling of theories. This gives a picture of man and nature which is on the whole a more Biblical one.

Exponents of the science of Man, called anthropologists, have been willing to revise theories and admit past mistakes. To a degree Biblical critics have done the same. The destructive theories of the nineteenth century denied the historicity of the larger part of the Old Testament, and cast doubt upon whether Abraham, Moses and others even existed. Since then archaeology has restored the general acceptance of the accuracy of the Bible record from Abraham's time to Moses and the Prophets. The Bible from Genesis 12 onwards has come back into its own.[1]

But what of the first eleven chapters? Have we reached a point of reassessment for them?

The spiritual truths embodied in the stories of origins in these chapters are of distinct importance in their own right, and their themes are worked out in the rest of the Bible. This makes this comparatively short section of scripture important to a degree out of all proportion to its length. If the leading personalities of the rest of the Old Testament could be said to be Abraham, Moses, the Kings and the Prophets, then the main character of the opening chapters must be Adam. But who was Adam? What new light has science to shed on him?

An identification based upon proper scientific method can now be made. The descriptions of the culture of Adam, the geography and topography of Eden, the origin of farming and animal breeding, the dispersal of this revolutionary *modus vivendi* from this centre to the world, have been borne out by our discoveries in such a manner as to warrant their historicity.[2]

[1] W. F. Albright, *The Biblical Period* (Blackwell, Oxford 1952) wrote (p. 3): "Until recently it was the fashion among biblical historians to treat the patriarchal sagas of Genesis as though they were artificial creations of Israelite scribes of the Divided Monarchy or tales told by imaginative rhapsodists around Israelite camp fires during the centuries following their occupation of the country. Eminent names among scholars can be cited for regarding every item of Genesis chapters 11 to 50 as reflecting late invention: or at least retrojection of events and conditions under the monarchy into the remote past, about which nothing was thought to be really known to the writers of later days. The archaeological discoveries of the past generation have changed all this. Aside from a few diehards among older scholars there is scarcely a single biblical historian who has not been impressed by the rapid accumulation of data supporting the substantial historicity of patriarchal tradition."

[2] See S. Cole *The Neolithic Revolution* (British Museum, 1963), pp. 1, 2, 13.

Anthropology has undergone some significant changes during the last two decades. Many anthropologists themselves are unaware that these changes are in a Biblical direction, and because there are so few theologians qualified in anthropology unfortunately theologians generally are unaware of these changes.

The works of Teilhard de Chardin, the priest-anthropologist have proved popular, but unfortunately his works were banned from publication for 25 years, and were written before these significant changes came about. Consequently, valuable though his works are, some themes are founded on premises no longer valid.

The change in anthropology is reflected in the fourth issue of L. S. B. Leakey's *Adam's Ancestors*. He says that important discoveries have necessitated the revision of earlier theories, and so instead of revising the earlier edition he has in fact completely rewritten the whole book.[3]

This change of outlook removes any necessity to quarrel with the general conclusions of either anthropology or geology. There have been fierce debates among anthropologists about present races and pre-historic races, and the interpretation of data, but on the whole they have been ready to revise their opinions when more revealing evidence has come in, especially so since the Piltdown fraud shock.

The exposure of the Piltdown fraud in 1953 is remembered by many. The Piltdown skull which had been discovered by Dawson in 1913 was tested for fluorine content and in other ways by Prof. J. S. Weiner and his colleagues.[4] As a result it was revealed that the skull was that of a modern type man (*Homo sapiens*). The jaw of an ape had been fitted to it, several teeth had been filed and stained to give a fossil appearance, and a canine tooth had also been filed to fit into a socket, and stained with chromate.

The Piltdown fraud was concocted upon the ideas current in 1913, but later became a puzzle to the anthropological world. The exposure came as a relief and also as a salutary lesson on the need for greater care and criticism of material. Formerly there had been a certain amount of gullibility in the anthropological world. For example, in 1922 Dr. Simpson found a tooth which he thought was near-human, and so he claimed it to be that of ape-man. The *Illustrated London News* published two full-page artist's impressions of male and female – all from a single tooth. Five years later it was found to be a pig's tooth. Again, Dr. E. Dubois, who discovered the famous Java-man fragments in 1891, revealed many years later in 1925 that he had kept back the Wadjak skull, which had a larger brain than the average modern man, i.e., 1,600 cc. He had

[3] L. S. B. Leakey, *Adam's Ancestors,* Fourth Edition (London 1953), Preface.
[4] J. S. Weiner, K. R. Oakley, Le Gros Clark, *The Solution of the Piltdown Problem* (Brit. Mus. 1953).

also hoarded five thighbones. Concerning this, Manchip-White says in the English Universities Press "Teach Yourself" series on Anthropology, "It was only many years later that the doctor, who was talented but somewhat peculiar, yielded up to the scientific world five thighbones that for some reason he had been hoarding."[5] Confidence in his other finds might have been undermined had not Koenigswald unearthed further Java-man remains, as they were called then.

Of course, a feature which has since been acknowledged is that Java man walked upright in perfectly human fashion. The museums had been depicting him with an ape-like stoop. Those thighbones might have saved them from this mistake. A more accurate analysis of other fossils showed that all known prehistoric man walked upright, but this fact was still to be appreciated at that time.

Perhaps a shock similar to the Piltdown exposure is needed in theology to shake some Bible critics into a frank re-examination of documentary theories about the Bible. These theories which reduce much of the Bible to folklore are over a hundred years old and are associated with the name of Wellhausen. They were formulated in ignorance of facts known today, yet some still cling to them tenaciously and jealously, if only in modified form. They were formed upon the same sort of Victorian assumptions which misdirected early anthropology. A score of theories in anthropology must have come and gone since then, yet Bible-criticism holds hard to theories formed in the comfort of Victorian studies, without any field knowledge of the literary methods of the Near East. Yet they are still presented as modern. K. A. Kitchen of Liverpool University Archaeological and Oriental Studies Department thinks that the "failure of Wellhausen and later contemporaries to heed evidence, is inexcusable."[6]

In contrast, anthropologists have been willing to learn. In the face of facts, they have abandoned the following theories:

a. *The Recapitulation Theory*. This postulated that the babe in the womb went through a series of developments re-enacting its evolutionary history from the fish, to monkey characteristics, and via ape to a fully human semblance before birth. This is now acknowledged to be unsupported by the facts of prenatal development.

b. *That man is descended from Monkeys*. One is still asked "Do you believe we descended from monkeys?" The questioner is surprised at the answer, "No anthropologist now believes this". The present position is that apes, monkeys, tarsiers, lemurs and tree-shrews were not our direct ancestors. It is thought that we may have had a long line of "common ancestors" whose fossils are at present undiscovered and from whom monkeys also branched off.

[5] J. E. Manchip-White, *Anthropology* (EUP 1960), p. 30.
[6] K. A. Kitchen, *Ancient Orient and the OT* (Tyndale Press, 1966), pp. 115 and 137.

c. It is not now held that larger brains and skulls indicate greater intelligence.

It is acknowledged that to draw pictures of a series of skulls with increasing brain capacity is misleading, as some human-like types living before our present race of man (*Homo sapiens*), had a bigger brain capacity. In any case our present race has a great variation of brain size (900–2,100cc.) It is, of course, the shape and convolutions which indicate brain potential and show to what species of early men the fossil belongs.

d. In contrast to earlier beliefs, it is acknowledged by anthropologists that earlier types of man (*hominids*) have died out, and that the variety of races who live on earth now, are all descended from one stock, namely, the more recent *Homo sapiens*.[7] This supports Paul's reference to the early chapters of Genesis:

> And God made from one stock every nation of men to live on all the face of the earth, having determined allotted periods and boundaries of their habitation (Acts 17:26).

e. It has been acknowledged that to represent older types of man as having an ape-like stoop is inaccurate. All museum exhibits have been altered to show that all fossil men remains reveal them as walking upright. (This has not been corrected in Russia, however).

f. The fossil bones of the hominids, which were formerly represented as ape-men, are now practically all re-named "*homo*" (meaning "man"). Correct measurements show that in spite of appearances of some, in all essential characteristics they are truly human. This goes even for the South and East African fossils, as Professor Le Gros Clark demonstrates especially with regard to the three cephalic indices typical of human-like skulls.[8]

g. It is now acknowledged that there existed "modern" types of men (*Homo sapiens*) long before our present race, e.g.:

Swanscombe Man – 200,000 years old.

Hungarian Man – 500,000 years old (found 1965).

Rudolph Man – 2,500,000 years old (found 1973).

Richard Leakey thinks his Rudolph skull, $2\frac{1}{2}$ million years old, challenges the theory of a simple view of human evolution. The Hungarian

---

[7] W. le Gros Clark, *Fossil Evidence*, Rev. Ed. (UCP 1964), p. 50: "It is now generally agreed that all the modern races of mankind are variants of one species, *Homo sapiens*."

So also: Raymond Firth *Human Types* (Mentor, 1963), p. 19; W. le Gros Clark, *Antecedents of Man* (Edinburgh 1959), p. 25; R. J. Harrison, *Man the Peculiar Animal* (Pelican, 1958), p. 52: "It is generally agreed that all human beings alive today fall into a single but polymorphic species, *Homo sapiens*. Most anatomists and anthropologists would also agree that all human beings that have lived on this earth during at least the past 10,000 years can be included in this one species"; and L. C. Dunn and Th. Dobzhansky, *Heredity, Race and Society* (Mentor, 1959) p. 122: "It looks as though the whole human race had got its genes from the same source."

[8] W. le Gros Clark, *Fossil Evidence*, Rev. Ed. (UCP, 1964) pp. 136–39. W. le Gros Clark, *Man-ape or Ape-man?* (Holt, Rinehart & Winston, 1967).

skull had a larger brain than modern man according to K. Oakley and J. Napier.[9]

These are not the first very early *Homo sapiens* to be found, but the anthropologist puzzled by such finds was inclined to explain them away and shelve them. As Manchip-White says, "They are placed in the somewhat crowded suspense account which is a noteworthy feature of the study of early man."[10] This attitude is changing, however. The principles of investigation set out in Le Gros Clark's *Fossil Evidence* reflect this change, which was demonstrated in the willingness to expose the Piltdown hoax.[11]

Leakey thinks that some of his East African finds which were placed on the suspension list, were also proto-Homo sapiens, and yet were contemporary with primitive types (*Unveiling Man's Origins*, Methuen, pp. 120f. 145, 161f.).

At the beginning of this chapter it was implied that in the light of recent discoveries, the setting to the story of Adam and Eve in Eden should be regarded as factual. Here again, in the realm of prehistoric archaeology we have a whole range of new facts.

However much or little of the story of Adam and Eve is pictorial, the point of prime importance is the apparent connection between Adam the farmer of Genesis 2 and the New Stone Age farmer of pre-history.

"The Lord God took man and put him in the Garden of Eden to *till* it and keep it." (Gen. 2:15). The particular connection of Adam and Eden with tillage – agriculture – is specifically mentioned three times. Garden farming, or horticulture, began in the Near East about 12,000 years ago. This is also where the Bible places its origin. This epoch-making event, the invention of farming, is called the New Stone Age Revolution. The term "mesolithic" is really obsolete. Before this, there had been types of man on the earth for half a million years, but they were all Old Stone Age men who had never discovered the secret of farming and of a settled existence. Consequently, they roamed the earth in search of wild food as hunter-gatherers.

Then the great New Stone Age Revolution took place at the end of the Ice-Age, in peri-glacial dry farming conditions as described in Genesis 2.

Man was able to control his food supply and so support villages and even New Stone Age cities, as described in Genesis 4, and discovered by Prof. James Mellaart in the Turkish Plateau west of the headwaters of the Euphrates.

The dispersion of the farmers from this centre to Europe, Africa, India and China, as described in the succeeding chapters of Genesis is also confirmed. Although it started 12,000 years ago, it did not reach

[9] Andor Thoma, "Vertesszollos Skull", *L'Anthropologie*, 1967, Vol. 70, Nos. 5 and 6.
[10] J. E. Manchip-White, *Anthropology* (EUP, 1960) p. 41.
[11] W. le Gros Clark. op. cit., Ch. 1.

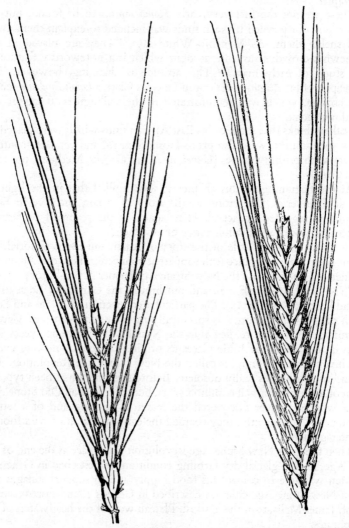

Fig. 1: Wild Grasses of the Middle East developed by man into cultivated wheats and barleys.

   (*left*) The diploid wheat *Triticum boeoticum*, wild ancestor of Einkorn; (*right*) *T. monococcum*, cultivated Einkorn. Approx. nat. size. *After E. Schiemann.*

England until 3,400 B.C., where the farmers established their large stand-ing-stone circles in order to celebrate agricultural fertility rituals. The classical example is Avebury Stone circle and ditch.

The evidence for this will be encountered later. It is in three main categories: Radio-carbon dating, Archaeology and Biology.

It is natural to ask how such knowledge of prehistory came to be recorded in the Bible so many thousands of years later. André Parrot, the French archaeologist, replied to a similar question, that "most of the traditions recorded in the first eleven chapters of Genesis were brought along by the patriarchs who emigrated from Mesopotamia."[12]

Prof. W. F. Albright of widely acknowledged authority, says in his book "New Horizons in Biblical Research" O.U.P. 1966: "They indubitably come from the same stock as corresponding ancient Mesopo-tamian traditions", and he refers to the Sumero-Accadian stories. "This means that there is good reason to believe the accuracy of the Israelite traditions which claim that their ancestors derive, in the main, from Mesopotamia." He says that the first eleven chapters of Genesis are in a special category of their own, and concerning the first chapter of Genesis, "We can safely say that this chapter will not be easily antiquated. The extraordinary thing is that it is more evolutionary in some respects than anything published before the early nineteenth century."[13] He means no doubt that it accords with the geological and biological record; the term "evolution" is used with a wide variety of meanings.

In contrast, we get a statement reported to have come from the Rev. Prof. W. Neil: "The Bible is not a reliable guide to astronomy, biology and similar scientific subjects since it was written in pre-scientific times by an unscientific people . . ."[14]

To say that a work is not a textbook on science is different from declaring that a book is scientifically inaccurate, yet that is often implied by similar statements. A person could write a book on a non-scientific subject and yet give evidence of a background knowledge of science.

For instance, there are on sale two children's books of animals; both are attractively produced. One appears to present the animals at random without scheme or order. The other indicates a knowledge of zoological taxonomy and the order of appearance of life on earth. The order in which the animals are presented in the latter would not convey this to the child enjoying her animals, but if she grew up to read zoology and happened to come across her childhood book she would recognize that the author had a greater depth of knowledge than was overtly apparent. He had

[12] André Parrot, *The Flood and Noah's Ark* (SCM, 1957), p. 44 and 45 footnote.
[13] W. F. Albright, *New Horizons in Biblical Research* (OUP, 1966), p. 8. This book gives the fruits of research since some of his bigger works.
[14] CEN, March, 1969.

been able to meet the simple pleasure of childhood and yet satisfy the sophistication of maturity.

Likewise, the Bible story of creation is presented for man's childhood in picturesque portrayal of the goodness of God in His Creation and purpose in man. But now that mankind has reached maturity in knowledge and science, an informed person can detect that in the story of Creation, the Creator's knowledge is endemic; the order of geophysics and biology is correct, though expressed in general and picturesque terms. (See chapters X, XI and XII of this book.)

The Bible may not have been written with the object of teaching science, nevertheless, the Bible is not unscientific, for hidden within its story is a Creator's knowledge. For this reason one would not agree with the phrase: "It was written ... by an unscientific people." This would appear to ignore the statements which run through the warp and woof of Scripture, that God made direct revelation of Himself to chosen individuals.

It will be noted that Albright did not suggest derivation from the Sumero-Accadian stories, but that all derive from the same source. We would suggest that the accounts in Genesis are from the original source, whatever form this might have taken until writing was invented.[15] K. A. Kitchen, lecturer in the School of Oriental Studies at Liverpool University, and a specialist in literary methods of the Ancient Near East writes, "The common assumption that the Hebrew account is simply a purged and simplified version of the Babylonian legend (applied also to the flood stories) is fallacious on *methodological* grounds. In the Ancient Near East, the rule is that simple accounts or traditions may give rise (by accretion and embellishment) to elaborate legends, but not vice versa. In the Ancient Orient, legends were not simplified or turned into pseudo-history (historicized) as has been assumed for early Genesis".[16] For this and other reasons to be given later, it is more likely that we have the original report in Genesis from which all others are derived.

The literary structure of Genesis is based upon eleven sections, each of which commences with the phrase "These are the generations of." The word "generations" is "*toledoth*" in the Hebrew, and refers to the origins of nations and races.[17]

---

[15] W. F. Albright, *Stone Age to Christianity* (Doubleday, 1957), pp. 64–81.

[16] K. A. Kitchen, *Ancient Orient and the O.T.* (Tyndale Press, Nov., 1966), p. 89.

[17] Albright writes: "Hebrew national tradition excels all others in its clear picture of tribal and family origins. In Egypt and Babylonia, in Assyria and Phoenicia, in Greece and Rome we look in vain for anything comparable. There is nothing like it in the tradition of the Germanic peoples. Neither India nor China can produce anything similar, since their earliest historical memories are literary deposits of distorted dynastic tradition, with no trace of the herdsman or peasant behind the demigod or king with whom their records begin. Neither in the oldest Indic historical writings (the Puranas) nor in the earliest Greek historians is there a hint of the fact that both Indo-Aryans and Hellenes were once nomads who immigrated into their later abodes from the north. The Assyrians to be sure, remembered vaguely that their

Ellicott in his commentary discussed the characteristics of a Genesis toledoth. He demonstrated that first there was a brief summary of what had preceded, and then a statement on what was to follow. This literary feature of Genesis thus formed a link between two sections.

Thus the statement in Gen. 2:4 "These are the generations of the heavens and the earth ..." is not a second account of creation, but a summary of Genesis 1, while the words which follow, "And every plant of the field" down to "and there was not a man to till the ground", are an introduction to the next instalment, which is the story of Eden and – we believe – New Stone Age Adam.

The eleven toledoths are thus the framework into which Genesis is fitted and are the true literary structure of Genesis (see p. 92 footnotes).

P. J. Wiseman elaborated upon Ellicott's insight with the suggestion, from his knowledge of Near Eastern literary methods, that the toledoth in Genesis was actually the link paragraph between tablets which Moses preserved in his compilation.

The characteristic of the toledoth is not dependent upon our acceptance of P. J. Wiseman's theory, however, although his theory is worthy of consideration.[18]

For him the toledoth is what is called a "colophon". When writing was made on tablets a link was made between a tablet and its sequel by a short passage summing up the contents and introducing the successive tablet. On the early tablets at the dawn of writing this colophon was written on the edge. Later – after 3000 B.C. – this colophon was written on the baked clay envelope into which the tablet was placed for protection.

In support that Genesis actually contains the record of early tablets, the topographical description of certain geographical areas were those of earlier times. This landscape had been altered by the time of Moses. For example, in Gen. 10:19 we read, "And the border of the Canaanites was from Sidon, as thou comest to Gerar, unto Gaza, as thou goest unto Sodom and Gomorrah ..."

This must have been written before the overthrow of Sodom and

---

earliest rulers, whose names they recalled without any details about their deeds, were tent dwellers, but whence they came had long been forgotten.

In contrast with these other peoples the Israelites preserved an unusually clear picture of simple beginnings, of complex migrations, and of extreme vicissitudes." (W. F. Albright, *The Biblical Period* (Blackwell, 1952), p. 3.)

[18] However the caution by D. Kidner should be observed: "By insisting on a complete succession of named tablets the theory implies that writing is nearly if not quite as old as man. Genesis itself read in any other way does not require this: it leaves it perfectly tenable that while the genealogies were committed to writing at an early but unspecified stage the rest of the family history may have been passed down by word of mouth as its manner often suggests. Some of the characteristics of oral tradition listed by E. Nielsen bring Genesis to mind, e.g. '... recurrent expressions, a fluent, paratactic style, a certain rhythm and euphony which are especially noticeable when one hears the account....' It is worth pointing out that this kind of transmission can be exceedingly accurate where it is in regular use." D. Kidner, *Genesis* (Tyndale Press, 1967), p. 24.

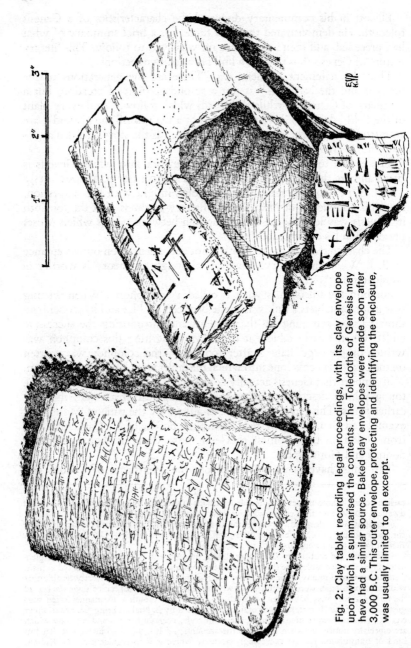

Fig. 2: Clay tablet recording legal proceedings, with its clay envelope upon which is summarised the contents. The Toledoths of Genesis may have had a similar source. Baked clay envelopes were made soon after 3,000 B.C. This outer envelope, protecting and identifying the enclosure, was usually limited to an excerpt.

Gomorrah by volcanic eruption 2000 B.C., for after Abraham's day the location was unknown until modern discoveries. These revealed that the site was submerged under the Dead Sea by the earth movement which was a typical rift-valley tectonic subsidence.

The simple monosyllabic Hebrew may preserve the primitive atmosphere of the early Sumerian sheathed clay tablets. The invention of writing by the Sumerians in the Protoliterary Epoch seemed to have been made by the temple priests *circa* 3500 B.C., in order to record the tithes given to God by the people. Writing had spread to Egypt by 3200 B.C., where it soon became indigenized into typical Egyptian, but Sumerian writing continued for another 1,000 years in Mesopotamia and Turkey, when it was superseded by Akkadian.

In the light of this, the conclusions of Professor A. S. Yahuda, who was Professor of Hebrew in the University of Madrid, are relevant. He states that words in early Genesis such as *"ed,"* or flood (Gen. 2:6), "Eve", "Eden", "rib", are Sumerian words. Alongside these words are Egyptian words such as *"tebah"*, meaning ark. These words occur nowhere else in the Old Testament except *tebah* in Exodus 2, which records Moses' own life in Egypt. He concludes that the patriarchs brought the stories from Mesopotamia (hence the Sumerian words) and Moses incorporated them in his records, which contained Egyptian words.[19]

The first two toledoths embodied in Genesis used to be taken as two separate stories of creation, the second starting in Genesis 2:4. Now that one can be regarded as a sequel to the other, the collation of anthropology with the Bible becomes possible. Thus Genesis 1 is a general introduction to the creation of man, both Old and New Stone Age, late in the sixth age-day, but it is left to the second toledoth to enlarge upon the appearance finally of the New Stone Age.

The Hebrew word *adam* supports such an interpretation. It is a generic noun meaning "man" or "mankind" in Genesis 1. In chapters 2 to 4 the definite article is added and it becomes "the Adam" or "the man" (or individual). From Genesis 3:17 onwards the noun also becomes an individual's name "Adam".

The third toledoth is a good summary of this development (Gen. 5:1–5 RSV). This man named Adam is the individual from whom our Lord's descent is eventually traced.

In the succeeding pages we shall use the name Adam to refer to this individual – a New Stone Age farmer of about 10,000 to 12,000 years ago.

"The Lord planted a garden in Eden . . . and there he put the man (or the Adam) whom he had formed . . . to till it and keep it."

---

[19] A. S. Yahuda, *The Language of the Pentateuch in its relation to Egyptian.* See also: W. J. Martin, *Stylistic Criteria and the Analysis of the Pentateuch* (Tyndale Press, 1955), p. 23.

CHAPTER II

WHY ADAM COULD NOT BE OLD STONE AGE MAN

THE MAIN DIAGNOSTIC FEATURE BY WHICH WE CAN IDENTIFY THE Adam of the Garden of Eden with any particular prehistoric race is the description of the culture the Bible gives as being that of Adam. A second feature is to identify the general geographical location and topography of this culture. Having decided upon what features are diagnostic, the structure we build upon these premises should be found to correlate harmoniously with such factors, as we discuss in chapters nine to eleven of this book.

To guide us to an answer to the question "Who Was Adam?", we find that Genesis 2–4 act as a type of cultural zone fossil. The main diagnostic character of the culture was that Adam cultivated crops, and bred animals. Such a clue should be a clear and unmistakable guide, as man had never practised farming before 10,000 B.C. or thereabouts.

A supporting culture clue is that the first use of metals had not yet commenced, for their discovery is noted later in Gen. 4:22. So this dates Adam as a New Stone Age farmer. It would appear also that we are in the first stages of farming. There is no mention of permanent buildings until later and there is still an element of berry and fruit gathering within that large area (unless it is cultivated trees which are referred to in Eden's garden). This would appear to place the time as being that of the first experiments when the farmers were still living in rock shelters and upon open sites – the era of the Shanidar sites and the Natufians.

It was man's major step forward to civilization. For 500,000 years it had never occurred to man to grow his own food. Then comparatively suddenly he became a farmer. He began to grow crops and breed farm animals, and thus by controlling his own food supply he was able to settle down to live in village communities.

Early man had to follow the migrations of the animals he hunted for his food supply, and constantly to seek fresh supplies of wild fruit and berries. In other words, he was a "Hunter-gatherer". The Hunter-gatherer may seem nearer to nature, but this insecure mode of life and culture could support only small roving bands. An uncertain food supply could never sustain large settled communities, as the American Plains Indians found to their cost.

As we have seen, prehistoric archaeology has demonstrated that the New Stone Age "Revolution" as it is called commenced in the Near East.

The place of origin of Old Stone Age Man on the other hand is thought to be East Africa, though others have suggested Central Asia.

It might be asked why this view has not been followed in the past. In the first place prehistory now presents a fuller picture. But the main reason may be that a certain degree of confusion existed in the minds of scientist Christians because they did not attempt to solve the problem of Adam's identity by the use of a correct method of analysis. They did not look for that diagnostic feature which would ensure a reliable identification.

Secondary questions have been allowed to confuse the issue such as: Do any of the humanoid types of the past 500,000 years show signs of desiring communion with God, or do they reveal a belief in the afterlife? Or which was the earliest to possess sufficient brain capacity to show moral responsibility and have a soul? Or, again, would it be possible that Adam lived so long ago as half-a-million years, or even two million? All such questions are based upon factors for which we have insufficient evidence in any case.

Can we be sure, however, that in the vast period of half-a-million years before New Stone Age farming no type of man cultivated crops or kept sheep and cattle? For the evidence, we must look at the tools and mode of living of these Old Stone Age men. Evidence that Old Stone Age man did not cultivate wheat and crops is demonstrated archaeologically by the complete lack of digging-stick weights, gardening hoes, corn-grinding querns, flint sickles polished by reaping, storage jars and baking ovens. It is demonstrated socially also by the lack of settled communities. All these, the New Stone Age men had. Old Stone Age implements were for hunting, or digging up roots. Their roving life took them from cave to cave, and for clothes they wore skins, sewn together with bone needles.

During that half million years or more, we have a worldwide record of stone tool-making. We can trace the development of the tool as man improved in the techniques of chipping stone into shapes.

Without the knowledge of metal, early man had to find a material which would give a hard and sharp point or cutting edge for his pursuits. It was siliceous stones which met these requirements, such as flint, volcanic glass called obsidian, and greenstone. They are far harder than iron. These were similar in texture to glass which we all know requires skill and training before a successful attempt to shape it is made. When a flint is chipped the resultant fracture is called a conchoidal fracture. On one side this is hollow and saucer-shaped, and on the other side it is convex with a bulge near where it has been struck. This is called the bulb of percussion. It takes considerable experience before blows can be struck with a "hammer stone" of the right texture so as to end up with a tool of the desired shape. In a sense, it is misleading to speak, as many do, of the "crude" tools of the Stone Age. Only the first pebble tools could be regarded as fairly simple, requiring only two chips off the pebble, but as anyone knows who has tried, to chip a pebble so as to leave a level cutting edge is quite difficult.

Consequently early men progressed slowly in developing more complicated tools, and at each stage they taught one another the shape and pattern which their techniques had achieved.

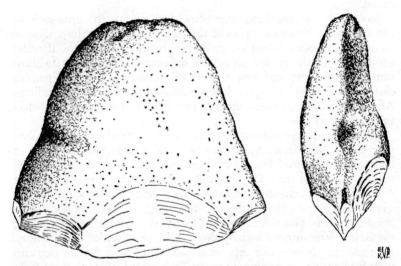

Fig. 3: A Pebble Tool associated with Australopithecinae, 600,000 B.C. The earliest known artifact made by a Hominid (i.e., a member of the human branch).

These patterns of tool-making became worldwide, with a few variations typical of Eurasia, India, Africa and China. This has made it comparatively easy for the prehistoric archaeologist to identify the age and general locality of the tool makers over half-a-million years. It also makes it easy to show that none of these tools was used for agriculture.

As we have said, man-made tools have been discovered which cover half-a-million years. The first are called "pebble" tools. These are made from pebbles about the size of one's fist. They have been found in Africa, Algeria and Morocco, and it is claimed that a few have been found in Europe and now possibly some in China.

The tool patterns which follow are of two main kinds. One is called a "core" tool. Here the main core of the block is used as the tool itself. The second kind is a "blade" tool, in which the pieces struck off the core are used as the tools.

The first culture using these two types of tools is called "Abbevillian", which lasted from the First Ice Age, about 500,000 years ago, to the Second Ice Age. The "core" tool is shaped by beating the block against a stone anvil. The flakes are named Clactonian flakes. The "core" tool is a sharp-pointed pear shape. The two faces are made by chipping off about eight

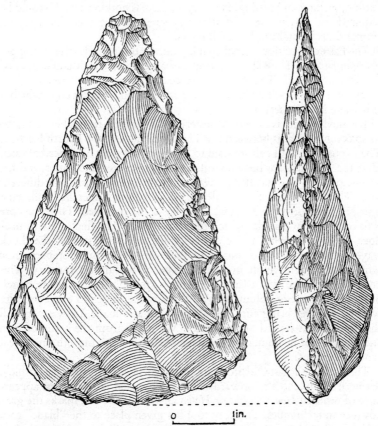

O   ⅟in.

Fig. 4 : Acheulean Hand-Axe, about 250,000 B.C. onwards. This one was associ-ated with Swanscombe man of the Old Stone Age (two-thirds size).

chips from each side. It has been called a hand-axe, but must have been an all-purpose tool.

The next culture is called "Acheulean". This lasted from the end of the Second Ice Age 350,000 years ago to the end of the Third Ice Age. The pear-shaped hand-axe gradually becomes less pointed as time goes on, and is shaped by chipping off as many as twenty flakes. This shows that skill was increasing. Eventually the shape of the tool becomes oval with quite a sharp cutting edge all round. Although such a tool still looks crude, it must have taken much experience and experiment to chip off pieces which would leave only shallow flat chip-scars. It is thought they managed this by hitting the block with a wooden club in order to obtain the correct percussion effect. These were used for chopping, scraping, cutting, picking and prising. Here again, there is nothing which would be required for agriculture, and the scrapers would be used for scraping animal skins brought in by the hunters.

The Eastern tradition of tool-making during this period is the "Chopper chopping-tool". They also made adze-shaped tools which could be used for shaping wood. The North-west coast Indians make most of their planks and totem-poles with adzes. An adze has one straight edge which is chisel-like in cross-section.

The next culture is called "Mousterian". This dates from about 150,000 to 50,000 B.C., that is between the Third Ice Age and the Fourth Ice Age. The Mousterian tool culture used to be associated with Neanderthal man. Here the hand-axe has become still more sophisticated and flatter, and has a twisted edge. This is called a "twisted ovate", and is varied for different jobs. The Mousterian flake-tool is produced by considerable skill. First a striking platform for the final blow has to be prepared. Then the core is flaked off at two angles which must be correct. The final blow to produce the tool must be at the correct angle and force so that the shock waves penetrating the elasticity of flint produce a bulb of percussion which fans out to result in a large flake of beautiful symmetry. This heart-shaped flake will then have two sharp thinly-acute cutting edges. Some have one edge blunted so as to allow the finger to exert pressure without the user being cut. The Mousterians also made side-scrapers. All the tool-kit was typical of the hunter. We know from the bones of man and animal that he hunted big game, especially the Mammoth, that great woolly elephant.

Then comes the last Old Stone Age culture, called "Upper-Palaeolithic", dating from 30,000 B.C. onwards. This is associated with the first appearance of modern *Homo sapiens* or *Homo sapiens sapiens*, and marks the great advance in techniques. The core tool has given place to the "blade" tool, which is capable of more diverse development. Quite a new technique seems to have developed comparatively suddenly. These tools can be made only from flint or obsidian. The stone block first has to be prepared into a cone shape, and then long blade-shaped flakes are whacked off the core vertically. These blades are skilfully adapted for a whole range of tools which would be equivalent to a hunter's knife, a chisel (burin or graver), an arrowhead (tanged point), a spoke-shave (notched blade), a drill or awl (borer), an end-scraper, a dagger, (laurel-leaf point), a wood plane (keel-shaped scraper), and a large wood plane (nose scraper).

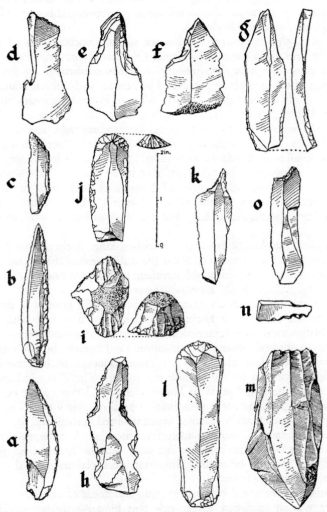

Fig. 5: Upper Palaeolithic Blade Tools, upper Old Stone Age, about 30,000 B.C., called by Miles Burkitt "The Magdalenian tool-kit". a.–c., Knives; d.–h., Chisels; i., Push-plane; j., Skin-scraper; k., Skin-piercer; l.–o., Planes, saw, and spokeshave.

Upper Palaeolithic man also developed tools from bone. Again there was a considerable variety. For fishing, they made double-pointed tanged spears, and also a detachable-headed harpoon. The modern Eskimo has similar fishing tackle. The detachable head which lodges in the fish is

attached to a long leather thong for the fisherman to haul in when the fish
has weakened. There are also carved thong-stroppers and bone needles of
the type used to sew skin clothes.

Again all this equipment is what we would associate with a hunter-
gatherer, and not a farmer. As Upper Old Stone Age man was so skilful an artist we have his hunting activities confirmed by his cave
paintings of the animals he pursued. The best are in Southern France and
in the middle of the Sahara Desert. When it became necessary to hunt
the smaller and swifter animals, lighter and more delicate arrowheads
were used with which to shoot them. To produce these and other implements, a skilful technique developed called "pressure-flaking",
and the small tools produced were called "micro-liths". It was discovered
that tiny chips could be taken off merely by pressing hard upon the
edge of the flint with a pointed bone stick. All sorts of delicate
shapes were achieved by the proud craftsmen who used to be called
Mesolithic (Middle Stone Age) but are now called proto-New Stone
Age.

Crabtree, the American expert in tool-making, declared that it took
him many years' experience to equal the craftsmanship of the Old Stone
Age tool-makers. Yet with all this excellent tool kit, not one is for farming
equipment. All are for the hunter-gatherer.

The Plains Indians are an example of the need for hunters to disperse
for survival. They are a fascinating example of a people who were
agriculturists until the seventeenth century, living in settled communities,
but they completely changed their culture and became buffalo hunters.
The cause of this dramatic change was the introduction of the horse to the
American continent by the Spanish conquerors. The Plains Indians discovered that mounted on swift horses, they could drive great herds of
thousands of buffalo to stampede into a corral or over a cliff. The meat
thus so easily and quickly obtained could be dried in strips and shared out
in abundant rations over the next few months. A tribe numbering
thousands would come together for this, and the leisure time which
ensued was spent in pow-pows, initiation rites, elaborate social organization, and prestige feasts.

Prestige was achieved by horse-stealing and deeds of valour.

Here was an exception to the rule that hunter-gathering could not
support large communities, but it was not a completely valid exception.
It still demanded a roving life to follow buffalo migrations over many
hundreds of miles. This is witnessed by the change in the type of dwelling
required. The wigwam replaced the house. Also the massing of population
was only a seasonal one from spring to autumn. When the buffalo season
ended, the tribe dispersed. One tribe endeavoured to avoid dispersion in
the off season, to see if they could eke out the rations. They almost
perished completely.

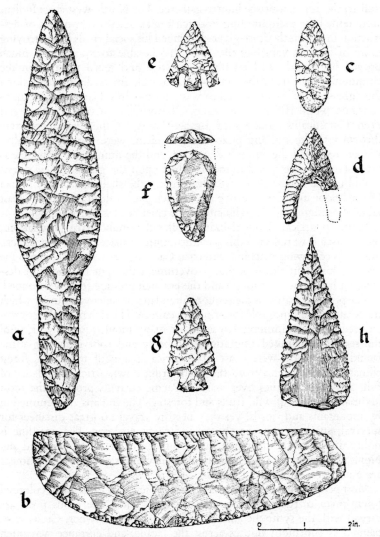

Fig. 6: Pressure-Flaked Tools of proto-Neolithic (Mesolithic), and Neolithic culture (10,000 to 5,000 B.C., in the Middle-East). Craftsmanship had reached a very specialised stage before the Bronze-Age. Exquisite and delicate shapes could be manufactured in siliceous stone by pressure-flaking and indirect percussion (half size). (a) Flint dagger; (b) Flint knife; (c), (d), (e) Arrowheads; (f) End-scraper; (g) American Indian arrowhead; (h) Australian spearhead.

Tools were ground smooth when the Neolithic culture matured.

There is, however, a culture of recent history which is a notable exception to the rule about the hunter-gatherer. The North-west coast Indians were famed for their amazing Potlatch Feasts. These were orgies of destruction in which the feast-giver challenged his social rivals by destroying more of his rich valuables than they. To be able to squander so much proved his wealth, and established prestige and social position in the community. Oil from the candle-fish, valuable for trading inland along the "grease trails", was poured to waste on the fires. Flames leaped up to consume wonderfully carved canoes, beautifully woven blankets, and even fantastically ornamented timber houses. Other valuables were thrown into the sea, and prized copper shields were broken up. Tally-keepers recorded the amount destroyed, and the number of gifts of sea-otter skins, blankets, and canoes lavished upon the guests. These guests would in due course amass wealth to return the challenge. Many a man became poor in order to prove he was rich and to sit higher up the feast table of prestige, and the winner became chief until superseded.

When American industrialization offered remunerative occupations, the potlatch feast reflected this acculturization. In place of native products, hundreds of sewing machines and even Cadillac cars were tipped into the sea. At this point the American Government thought this orgy of destruction had gone far enough and the potlatch prestige feast was banned.

The potlatch feast was the result of abundance in an environment which made such wealth possible for primitive culture. The rich natural resources enabled a large community to settle for many months in the year, until the season for limited migrations for berry and root gathering came round. The north-west coast of America is a cool temperate forest climate. Cold currents from the north bring down a rich abundance of fish, and the westerlies over warmer Pacific currents produce the most luxuriant growth of wild fruits and forestry. The Indians are hemmed in by mountains and fjords, yet they need to travel no great distances for survival, spoilt as they are by an indulgent ecology. The coastline is rather similar to the drowned valleys and fiords of N.W. Scotland and Norway. Backed by high mountains, their villages of great plank houses are built upon the friendly shores.

Most people have seen pictures of their grotesquely carved and coloured totem-poles reared up before their houses. These enormous posts are carved with the symbolic animal crests of the house-owner. Crests were painted as enormous figures across the façade, and entrance was often through the gaping mouth of a monster. An amusing modern touch was seen recently. At one of these entrances was hung a notice "No admittance to Anthropologists." After all, there are more of them in America than here!

The houses were constructed from great red and yellow cedars. Smaller houses were forty feet square, but others extended to several hundreds of feet in length. They were built on a massive framework footed by an earth bank. The walls were made of great vertical planks which they split by bone wedges. The roofs were given the appearance of large corrugations from the alternating overlapping concave and convex roof boards. These were gouged out by ground adzes. The roof and wall planks were rather like those of the Hebrew Tabernacle in the wilderness, and could be taken down individually and transported to different sites during seasonable migrations, but the framework of house and village remained for the return.

The wealth of the sea consisted of halibut, cod, herring, and summer runs of migrating salmon swarmed up the inlets to their upstream breeding grounds. Abundant candle-fish gave edible oil in the spring, and great sea mammals, whales, sea-lions, sea-otters, seals and porpoises were hunted with bone harpoons.

This culture was of New Stone Age origin as their ground stone tools show, but they give us a vivid picture of any Stone Age fishers. They used shell hooks for line fishing, bone spears, points, barbed prongs, nets, and a "fish-rake". The latter had many points on a flat pole which the fisherman thrust through a shoal of herring, so close packed that several would be impaled upon the points.

For whaling, after much magic to combat the dangers, the chief harpooner with picked crews would set out in their dug-out canoes. Their weapon was a large, stout-headed harpoon. This had a triangular shell point and barbs of antler, and was wedged into a heavy yew shaft ten feet long. It detached itself when thrust home into the whale, and the line of whale sinew ran out to many fathoms, eventually to be pulled in when the capture was exhausted.

There are several interesting factors in this culture which should serve as a caution to anthropologists when interpreting archaeological remains. In many ways they were advanced people. Their arts, crafts, and skills are to be admired, yet they are a Stone Age people. If one were to discover their utensils and products archaeologically after say a quarter of a million years, one would find that very few of their materials had survived. There would be, of course, their stone adzes – a kind of hoe with a chisel-like cutting edge. One would have to guess that these were used for chipping their long house-planks from tree trunks. All their cooking vessels were made of wood. Their food was boiled by dropping red-hot stones into these vessels, which being wooden could not be placed over a fire. At a big feast a whole dug-out canoe was used as a cooking vessel. The contents were kept boiling by a constant procession of Indians dropping in heated stones.

This elaborate and colourful society should warn us not to judge prehistoric man as crude because of the apparent simplicity of surviving tools.

A point emphasized by Oxford anthropologists was that the N.W. Coast Indians should be compared with other primitive communities living in similar conditions elsewhere in the world. We would then see that brain potential and a promising environment do not inevitably promote an advanced society.

Take, for example, the Fuegans and Auraucanians of the southern tip of S. America. They are, of course, *Homo sapiens*, as are all people in the world today. They have the same rich fishing grounds and ecology, yet Darwin described them as the most backward of races, indolent and without houses. He thought it impossible to educate them but he reckoned without the South American Missionary Society who set to work there. Their work brought about a great change in the hearts of these primitives. Many were educated, and some were ordained as ministers. Darwin was amazed, and for the rest of his life gave an annual donation to this Missionary Society which is still working effectively today.

Professor Daryll Forde points out that the primitive Tasmanians were a more obvious case in point. They were even more backward culturally, yet lived in an ecology similar to N.W. Indians, and failed to exploit it.[1]

Today anthropologists do not measure intelligence by brain capacity when thinking of fossil man. Cultural development and continuance are greater factors, and these are not an inevitable evolution dictated by environment. The fact that pre-Adamites did not progress beyond Old Stone Age culture had little to do with brain capacity. Even *Homo sapiens* Swanscombe man of 200,000 years ago was characterized by the tool habit of his time, which was Acheulean. Yet he had a brain identical with modern *Homo sapiens* except that he had a thick skull, which was the only sense in which he could be called "thick-headed"! Neither can environment alone account for Adam's great discovery, for earlier men had similar conditions of terminal ice phases at various times. Was it because they lacked the Divine instruction to till the ground? Whatever the reason they do not qualify to be interpreted as Adam of Eden because of the absence of farming techniques in their culture.

[1] C. Daryll Forde, *Habitat, Economy and Society* (Methuen, 1963), p. 100.

CHAPTER III

THE PLACE OF OLD STONE AGE MAN

NOWHERE IN THE BIBLE ARE WE TOLD HOW LONG AGO ADAM WAS created. Archbishop Ussher of the early seventeenth century made a calculation based upon the genealogical tables of the Bible. Some anthropologists love to quote him to infer the ludicrousness of his dates, but forget the many revisions that anthropologists have had to make of their own calculations. Early this century William Solus' time for the appearance of early man, for example, was only 65,000 years ago. Zeuner in the 1950's extended this to 500,000 years, and now those who follow Leakey give 2 million years. These estimations are for the age of the same creatures.

Actually, the much-maligned Ussher might be less wide of the mark than anthropologists in view of the evidence that Adam was Neolithic Man of 12,000 years ago. Ussher placed Adam 6,000 years ago, thus making it a matter of thousands of years rather than millions.

Our knowledge of genealogical methods practised among Arabians may indicate that genealogies should not be calculated in the manner adopted by Ussher. The phenomenal ages given to the patriarchs could be regarded as royal houses so to speak like Tudors, Stuarts, Hanover, in which only the founder of the house figures, and the last generation between houses recorded. In confirmation of this, King David's genealogy of Ruth 4:18–22, is selective, and so is that of our Lord's in Matthew 1. This is not the only possible explanation, but whatever the explanation may be, the Bible range of time seems to be about right for the appearance of Farmer Adam (Camping's method dates Adam at 11,000 B.C.).

W. F. Albright says concerning genealogies: "Ancient and modern Arab genealogies, together with similar examples from Rhodesia, Hawaii, as well as from many other places, usually start with the putative ancestors of the clan. After several generations there are long gaps, followed by the latest ten generations or so – the generations in between are omitted without explanation. Historical analogy suggests that the same may be true of the Biblical genealogies."[2]

If the Adam of Genesis 2 was New Stone Age, and lived only some 10 or 12 thousand years ago, the question arises why the Bible does not tell us about the vast stretch of pre-history of other types of man before Adam? After all, half-a-million years is no small span.

To take the more obvious answer first: Scripture is not intended to

[2] W. F. Albright, *New Horizons in Biblical Research* (OUP, 1966), p. 11, footnote.

satisfy our curiosity about other creations, either earlier on earth or on other planets. Scripture is concerned with the salvation of our own present race which now occupies this world: the Black, Yellow and White (and possibly, Brown), which anthropologists agree are descended from one stock, and which need the redemption God has provided in Christ.

This explanation could be sufficient, but a second answer is that Old Stone Age man appears mainly to be referred to earlier in Genesis. It should, however, be clearly understood that the identity of Adam as of New Stone Age culture does not depend upon whether mankind in Genesis 1 can be proved to be Old Stone Age. There is far too little detail in the first chapter, but the fact that what little is said fits in so consistently, adds weight. It is the culture of Genesis 2 which is the diagnostic factor.

A careful examination of the text of Gen. 1:26–31, gives us a picture of the hunter-gatherer. The cultural description fits and it is correctly positioned before the story of Adam of Eden.

We find that God's terms of reference to Old Stone Age man are different from those given to Adam. Adam's allotted purpose is to lead a settled life in Eden's horticultural plots. Old Stone Age man by contrast is to lead a roving life, to "fill the earth and subdue it". "Subdue" implies the slaying of wild animals for food. It implies wild beasts which need subduing. It also implies a superior intelligence of the hunter's skill, who, although his body is defenceless against fangs, claws, horns and tusks, can make tools with which to manufacture weapons to kill and subdue animals. He is "Man the Toolmaker", a phrase coined by Kenneth Oakley of the British Museum.[3]

"Let them have dominion over the fish of the sea" we read in Genesis 1. They did so by their bone and flint harpoons, fishing-lines and shell hooks, and casting nets and launching fishing-boats and kayaks. Old Stone Age man became adept in fishing, as we have seen from our survey of the culture progress. At the Poisson rock-shelter near Les Eyzies there is sculptured on the ceiling in low relief a fish with a ring in its nose.

"Let them have dominion over the birds of the air" with their tombolas – round stone weights on string which when thrown into the air cleverly entangled the legs of the birds and brought them down; or the light blow-pipes and darts, and baits and nets and boomerangs.

"Let them have dominion over the cattle." Cave paintings of Southern France (Provence) and Sahara depict in wonderful polychrome art, the lively bisons and stampeding mammoth elephants, and mark accurately the vital organs which arrow and spear must pierce for speedy killings.[4] Even as armies need drill and discipline to steel their nerve, so too the hunter primitives probably carried out their sympathetic magic in

[3] K. Oakley, *Man the Toolmaker* (British Museum, 1961).
[4] A. Laming, *Lascaux* (Pelican, 1959).

ritualistic horn and stag dances. These beautiful paintings are now popular for designs on articles for household use and decoration.

The earth was to be filled by man as well as subdued, and dominion was to be "over all the earth and over every creeping thing." Biologists have remarked that man is the most ubiquitous animal on earth. He adapted himself to every climatic region which he occupied, whereas most animals are confined to their particular environment and fill their ecological niche. That Old Stone Age man travelled far is evidenced by his tools. We have seen how the tool techniques covered all the old world, and had two main traditions of pattern associated with East and West. *Homo sapiens* did not reach the American Continent until about 25,000 years ago.

Old Stone Age man was also a gatherer of fruit and berries and a digger of roots with his "hand axes". This characteristic is reflected in the words "I have given you every plant yielding seed . . . every tree with seed in its fruit, for food." Some were vegetarians (herbivorous) and others meat-eaters (carnivorous).

Perhaps moral responsibility was not fully given, for whereas Adam of the New Stone Age was forbidden a certain fruit, to Old Stone Age men God says they could eat of all the trees (Gen. 1:29). But communication with God, and speech, seem indicated by the words "God said to them." There must have been an effective means of communication, probably by speech, for them to give this world-wide teaching of toolmaking which was passed on from generation to generation.

Thus the text gives us a picture of the hunter-gatherer, who was forced to scatter far and wide in small groups.

"Fill the earth," said the Lord, " . . . over all the earth have dominion."

The evidence for the existence of Old Stone Age man for half-a-million years is more convincing from the discovery of his tools than from the comparatively few skeletal remains associated with these. Koenigswald remarked at a meeting of the Fellows of the Royal Anthropological Institute that all the fossil-bone fragments would only cover two tables. In contrast, Stone Age tools are scattered in their thousands throughout the world. For example, they are scattered throughout East Anglia, and yet there has not yet been found a single skull or fossil-bone. It looks almost as if they had a resurrection!

Some Christian writers untrained in anthropology have argued about headshapes of prehistoric man. They have attempted to account for them by disease or distortions, but knowledge of cephalic indices rules their objections out of order. In any case these tool cultures are a far more indisputable evidence that pre-Adamites really existed.

Father Patrick O'Connell reviews the fossil remains in a very useful critique, but he declares they are frauds or distortions. This method ignores the extensive tool culture succession, and when one has actually examined the fossils, it is quite evident that there are consistent primitive types. Nevertheless, his work is valuable. It not only gives some inside information, it also develops one's critical faculty.[5]

Other scientific Christians, such as those of the American Scientific Affiliation who contributed to the symposium "Evolution and Christian Thought Today", have set out the data and discussed the problems, in a scholarly and useful manner, but they looked for the writing of some other work to guide the Christian on how to relate these to the Bible.[6]

Even as far back as mid-Victorian times there have been those of fundamentalist outlook who have seen the possibility that pre-Adamites existed. This is demonstrated by the fact that G. H. Pember wrote his "Earth's Earliest Ages" well before fossil remains of palaeolithic man had been found or acknowledged. He thought that Scripture indicated that there were races of men before our own. His conclusion was drawn from remarks made by the prophet Ezekiel, and from other passages of scripture. "Why," he wrote, "if a pre-adamic race really existed upon earth do we not find some indications of it among the fossil remains? Certainly no human bones have been as yet detected in primeval rocks; though if any should be hereinafter discovered, we need find no contradiction to Scripture in the fact."[7]

The terms Old and New Stone Age refer to the type of culture as seen in the tools, and other artifacts, dwellings and means of livelihood of man. They do not refer to the types of humans themselves. The four or five species of man who have succeeded each other in the earth will be described in the next chapter.

Old Stone Age is sometimes called Palaeolithic from *palaios*, old, and *lithos*, a stone. New Stone Age is also called Neolithic from *neos*, new.

African anthropologists and some Americans give the time range for the Old Stone Age as being 2,000,000 years. Europeans take it as 500,000 or perhaps 600,000 years. These are differences of opinion on how long the Ice Ages lasted, for it was during them that human-like types made their appearance.

There were four invasions of ice during the Ice Ages. Geologically the epoch is called Pleistocene and regarded as lasting nearly one million years. The calculation of the length of the Ice Ages is under constant revision, and so anthropologists like to relate the age of a man-like fossil to its position within those Ice Ages, but for the general reader this is confusing and so we shall give instead time lengths and datings on the European scale.

[5] P. O'Connell, *Science of Today and the Problems of Genesis* (Radio Replies Press Soc., USA, 1959).
[6] Carl F. H. Henry, "Theology and Evolution", *Evolution and Christian Thought Today*, Ed. R. L. Mixter. Symposium of members of the American Scientific Affiliation (Paternoster P., 1959), p. 221.
[7] G. H. Pember, *Earth's Earliest Ages* (Hodder & Stoughton, 1876), p. 73.

As half-a-million years have been allotted to Old Stone Age man, it will be asked where this fits in with six days of creation in Genesis. The duration of Old Stone Age culture in science may be correlated with a mere fraction of a day at the end of the sixth day in Genesis.

Many Christian geologists do not take a day of creation as meaning twenty-four hours, but as representing a great period of time on the geological scale. This is not a manipulation to suit modern knowledge, as is shown by the fact that even Augustine in the fifth century suggested that the days of Genesis were great lengths of time. He reached this conclusion in a pre-scientific age through the examination of the text itself.

Moreover, Moses himself speaks of the creation days as being great periods of time in Psalm 90, "The Psalm of Moses". The famous hymn by Isaac Watts is a paraphrase of it: "A thousand ages in Thy sight are like an evening gone." The Psalm speaks of the vastness of time as being appropriate for the God of eternity who formed the earth:

> Lord, thou hast been our dwellingplace in all generations.
> Before the mountains were brought forth, or ever thou hadst formed the earth and the world, even from everlasting to everlasting, thou art God.
> Thou turnest man to destruction; and sayest, Return ye children of men.
> For a thousand years in thy sight are but as yesterday when it is past, and as a watch in the night.

A similar thought is expressed by the Apostle Peter in his Second Epistle. (II Pet. 3:8).

The Hebrew word *yom* for "day" is, like ours, variously used, as it is in Gen. 2:4. Here creation is also spoken of, but the word "day" refers to a different period of time altogether. In general use we speak of the "people of today"; obviously not meaning a day of the week.

Kidner's Commentary on Genesis says, "The AV's 'the evening and the morning were' gives the misleading impressions that the reckoning starts with evening. Rather translate it 'evening came and morning came' (Moffatt; cf. RV, RSV)."[8] This places the emphasis on the end of one era and the beginning of another, rather than upon the length of the period.

It is sometimes objected that as the Sabbath rest commanded for the human race was a 24-hour day, the divine rest upon which it was founded must have been only 24 hours.

A little reflection on this ought to show that the length of man's day should be relative, for the human life-span is so brief compared with the God of Eternity.

There is also another very realistic reason why God's day and man's day should be different. To put it crudely, God does not live on our

[8] D. Kidner, *Genesis* (Tyndale Press, 1967), p. 47.

planet! Does He then measure the length of His own rest by earth's rotations rather than by those of any of the other planets, or even by a universal day in star-systems which revolve once in billions of years? As the light in Gen. 1:3 must be cosmic light the days are more likely to be cosmic days.

Some would see difficulty in thinking of God resting for a whole age if the age-day interval were applied to the seventh day. Now it is essential to observe what sort of work it was from which God rested on the seventh day. He rested from all his work of creation. In other words, He made nothing new. It is patent that no new orders of animals have been initiated from the time of man's appearance in the Pleistocene to this day. If God's work in the six days was the work of creating and making matter, life and organisms, it is reasonable to assume that His rest on the seventh day is a *rest* from the making of such organisms. In other words, He has been "resting" for many thousands of years. For those who think our Creator's Sabbath was a twenty-four hour day, the logic is to ask "What happened after the seventh day"? God's seventh day cannot be said to end unless we are told that God commenced work again, and a list of the second week's creative activities given. But no such statement is made, and so from the literalist's own logic it may be assumed that God's Sabbath rest still continues until the Lord says "Behold I create a new heaven and new earth!" which is still in the future (Isa. 64: Rev. 21). We see then that God's rest in material creation has already extended many thousands of years, though the genetic mechanism which He set in motion through the chromosomes and genes and DNA of meiotic cells (the seed of plant, animal and man) (Gen. 1:11, 21 & 24), continue to adapt themselves, within the genetic code, to their environment.

The Hebrew root for resting means to desist, not to rest. Accordingly, Jesus said "My Father works until now, and I work". He referred to spiritual re-creation in man, for we are told, "If any man be in Christ, he is a new creation". The rebirth by the Holy Spirit is a miracle in a man's nature, but God's rest must be understood in the same terms as those of His activity at the time, and that activity in Genesis concerned the natural order.

CHAPTER IV

PRE-ADAMIC FOSSILS

ALTHOUGH THE CONVINCING EVIDENCE FOR THE EXISTENCE OF PRE-Adamites comes from the world-wide distribution of Palaeolithic tools, their species are classified by their fossils. These skeletal remains are the human types referred to in Genesis 1 who lived before Adam of Eden.

As shown by Le Gros Clark, in all diagnostic features they were true men.[1] They walked upright, their head measurements were fully human in essential characteristics, and so were their dental arcades. A very important feature was that they had a long childhood which a human brain needs for learning. This is seen from the order of eruption of the teeth. In the light of this, it is misleading of artists to draw a furry face, and an ape-like muzzle for a nose. It would be a safer guess and in keeping with other characteristics to draw human skin, beard and nose; and to give a dignity and bearing to his walk. The contrast of a human foot with that of an ape is very great. The transverse and longitudinal arches enable man to walk with upright balance and to walk on two legs for miles, which would be impossible for an ape.

Let us imagine that we are watching an ape in a zoo. The orang would

Fig. 7: Misleading Artist's impressions of Australopithecus. This African humanoid is the most misrepresented hominid of all. It is usually drawn to look very apelike. The top is as drawn for *Sunday Times*, April 5, 1964; the bottom as drawn for *National Geographic*, September, 1960. The second drawing is more likely to be nearer actuality, because the fossil remains are humanoid in all essential indices.

[1] W. le Gros Clark, *Man-ape or Ape-man?* (Holt, Rinehart & Winston, 1965).

walk over to you with an ungainly motion. His forward sloping body places the centre of gravity over his shoulders, so that he uses his long arms as extra legs, his bent knuckles acting as the soles of the feet. If you contrast him with the zoo keeper, you would see how the keeper stands and walks upright on his two legs, leaving his arms and hands free for other jobs. To enable the keeper to have such perfect balance, the whole of the human frame is drastically modified by comparison with that of the ape. The human foot has three arches of bones and ligaments, making a three-point contact with the ground. The ape's foot is floppy, so to speak; its toe is more like a fat thumb. Man's big toe and phalange extends the whole length of his foot, and is bound firmly to the other toes and meta-tarsals (little bones in the foot), forming a strong longitudinal arch, completed at the back by a heel such as is lacking in the ape.

The longitudinal arch of man's foot ensures that weight is spread evenly, and allows the foot to be used as a strong flexible lever. When we see the spring in man's step, we see what the arches in his feet are doing for him, so that eleven stone of weight on one foot does not jar the body. The arches work even harder when he runs and jumps.

The specialized structure carries on up the leg bones with the joints or condyles at a fitting angle. The ball and socket joint fits into the pelvis so that a deep sciatic notch is behind it to enable man to walk upright. This deep notch is lacking in the ape. The small of the back is arched concavely to support the rib cage. If it arched forwards like the ape's, man would never stand upright. At the top of the spine, there is a universal joint which connects with the base of the skull. This joint or bearing is half way along the base of the skull to give perfect balance for upright walk, and to enable man to look straight ahead with his eyes level with the horizon. The discovery of any part of a skeleton can thus indicate whether it is human or ape.[2] There are additional characteristics which divide palaeo-lithic men into their four taxonomic groups.

The geological layer or stratum in which fossils are found is one of the ways of determining their age. Other ways are by measurement of fluorine content, radioactivity, and the species of cold or warm climate animal-remains with which they are in association. Varves, which are sediments left by successive summer glacial ice-melts, glacial deposits, and the succession of levels left by rivers during their downcutting of valleys, are also of great importance.

There is the belief in some quarters that the Ice Ages or Pleistocene times during which man had appeared were only one brief period. This theory supposed that geological strata during these times had been so overturned that geologists had been deceived in their interpret-ation.

One should not dismiss any theory without examination. It is for the

[2] R. J. Harrison, *Man the Peculiar Animal* (Pelican, 1958), pp. 158–74.

specialist in Pleistocene Geology to test the reliability of his dating techniques.

The chronology of Pleistocene Geology is a specialist subject because additional types of evidence to those used in the more general geology have to be employed. Pleistocene Geology concerned only one million years, whereas the geological column was concerned with fossils over a range of 600 million years.

How do these standard tests help us to date the age of fossil men?

The advance and retreat of the Ice Ages is evidenced by the cold or warm climate animals and plants which lived or grew during these phases. These animals and plants are divided mainly into the classifications of Sub-arctic, Temperate Forest and Steppe, and Hot Climate. The association of these animals with fossil man identifies the period in the Ice Ages with which he is connected.[3]

The fluorine test reveals whether the fossils in any one stratum are of the same age as each other, but it is not a means whereby the age of the specimens can be measured. In other words it is useful for relative dating but of no guidance to absolute dating. The fluorine test is possible because bones absorb fluorine from percolating waters. The longer the bone remains *in situ*, the higher is the percentage of fluorine absorbed. However, the percentage also depends on the amount of fluoride in the water percolating through any one area, hence the dating can be only relative for that area. If there is a discrepancy between two bone remains in one provenance, it means that one is an intrusion.

River terraces give self-evident chronology. As rivers cut down and wear away a valley, they leave terraces. Any fossils on these terraces can be dated according to whether they are on a later or earlier terrace.

Glacial deposits come into a similar category, but take more unravelling, although the succession of sites in East Anglia seems conclusive.[4]

A good example of how complementary methods can combine to give an accurate dating is the case of the Swanscombe man, a *Homo sapiens* of some 200 thousand years ago. (Anthropologists prefer to define the time as being during the Great Interglacial rather than to give a time in years). The bones were on the 100-foot Middle-Pleistocene terrace of the Thames under twenty-four feet of undisturbed well-stratified gravels. The animal remains correlated as being temperate forest Middle-Pleistocene Fauna. The flint implements also correlated, being of the Middle Acheulian hand-axe industry. In addition, the fluorine analysis of the bones gave a content of two per cent fluorine, which equated well with the mammals of the Swanscombe terrace.

Radioactive tests are by Carbon 14 and Potassium-argon. The amount

[3] F. E. Zeuner, *Dating the Past* (Methuen, 1958).
[4] West and McBurney, "Hoxne", *Proc. Prehistoric Soc.* (London, 1955). D. Baden-Powell, *British Regional Survey of E. Anglia* (London, 1956), Vol. 2.

of the radioactivity remaining in a specimen is measured. The rate of decay is known – for example the half-life of Carbon 14 is 5,730 years[5], the quarter-life is 11,000 years, and so on until there is less and less to measure. Carbon 14, therefore, can measure usefully only up to about 30,000 years. The half-life of Potassium-argon is much longer, being $1\frac{1}{4}$ million years, and is used to measure specimens over ten million years old.

This leaves an unfortunate gap in radioactive dating. It explains why the American claim to have dated Leakey's Australopithecinae at two million years by potassium-argon is not accepted by European anthropologists.[6]

The accuracy of Carbon 14 dating is based upon its immutable rate of decay. Archaeologists have to make sure, however, that their sample has not been contaminated by adjacent specimens.

There is also another factor which should be considered. A basic assumption is that radiation from the sun has always continued at the same rate, but Stuiver demonstrated in 1970 that from 5,500 to 10,000 years ago the level of atmospheric C. 14 was from 7% to 10% higher than present, perhaps through changes in the earth magnetic dipole moment. He checked C. 14 dating against varve sequences which shortened dates by 800 years per 10,000 years. On the other hand, Suess' bristlecone-pine dating is apt to lengthen them by the same amount. One should have this in the back of one's mind as a possible modification of the dates in this book.[7]

The result of using these means of relative and absolute dating gives us the following picture of the types and species of Stone Age Man.

The earliest and oldest are at the bottom because the older rocks or strata in which they are found are lower than the more recent.

5. *Homo sapiens sapiens* (Modern type man) from 30,000 years ago;
4. *Homo neanderthalensis* is 150,000 to 40,000 years ago;
3. *Homo sapiens Swanscombe man* – 200,000 years ago;
2. *Homo erectus* of China, Java and now found elsewhere – 300,000 years ago;
   (Now the *Hungarian Homo sapiens* which is as old as Australopithecinae and the *Rudolph Homo sapiens*, $2\frac{1}{2}$ million years old, have to be fitted in.)
→ 1. *Australopithecinae* of South and East Africa, 500,000 years ago.

It will be noticed that all the above are now given the general prefix *Homo* which means 'man'. Earlier anthropologists up to 1955, regarded

---

[5] As revised 1967 by the International Atomic Energy Agency.

[6] This gap may be closed by Helium-Uranium dating and Thorium dating: *Radioactive Dating and Methods of Low-level Counting*, Proceedings of a Symposium organized by the International Atomic Energy Agency (Vienna, 1967), pp. 313, 395–402.

[7] "Tree ring, varve, and C. 14 chronologies," *Nature* Oct. 31, 1970. W. E. Suess, Bristlecone-pine Cal. C. 14 Var. 308.

types 1 to 4 as more or less ape-men. Now they are regarded as having all the essential human characteristics, even including No. 1 – Australopithecinae, who lacks the prefix 'Homo' (although Leakey did name one branch 'Homo habilis', justified by a USA expedition in 1967).

As Le Gros Clark says, the name Australopithecinae, meaning "Southern Ape", is misleading as it is no longer regarded as an ape, and has nothing to do with Australia.

Thus it will be noticed that whereas up to fairly recently, anthropologists thought they had a number of ape-man fossils, the position now is that we have none. Anthropologists hope that they may find some, but at the moment there is a twenty-million-year gap to the nearest generalized fossil ape. It was found by Dr. Leakey in East Africa, who named it Proconsul, as he thought it might be ancestral, but it should be remembered that this is definitely a small ape.

It should be remembered also that specimens in the list 1 to 5 are not considered ancestral to each other. They are all considered to have come independently from a chain of unknown generalized ancestors whose fossils have not yet been found. So it is more than a missing link we have today. It is a whole missing chain! The 10,000-year gap between *Homo neanderthalensis* and *Homo sapiens* should be noted. A reinterpretation of the caves of Mt. Carmel by Higgs and Brothwell has now been generally accepted.[8]

The reason why fossils 1 to 5 are not considered linked is because each has developed a specialized feature, which the later species above it does not possess, and therefore could not have developed from it.

This means, of course, that the present *Homo sapiens* race now inhabiting the earth has no known fossil link with anything before it. The existence of such links is only assumed as being necessary to the theory of evolution. If anyone wanted to believe that the present race upon earth was a completely new start by God, there is no empirical scientific fact to prevent his doing so. In fact, Dr. Garlick, the fossil expert, said that the origin of the present human race of *Homo sapiens* is more of a mystery than ever.

The types of men listed above were thought at one time to be typical of their own particular region, but the discovery of fossils of each type in other parts of the Old World show that they each successively had a world-wide spread. As Howell says: "All the available evidence can be interpreted as indicating that in spite of much geographical variation, never more than one species of man existed on the earth at any one time."[9]

In America the earliest Palaeolithic did not arrive until 23,000 B.C. It seems unconnected to the later neolithic primary mongoloids, i.e. the

[8] D. R. Brothwell, "The People of Mt. Carmel", *Proc. Prehist. Soc.*, 27: 155, 1961.

E. Higgs, "Some Pleistocene Faunas of the Mediterranean Coastal Areas", *Proc. Prehist. Soc.*, 27: 144, 1961.

[9] J. Howell, "Middle Pleistocene", *Current Anthropology* (USA, 1961).

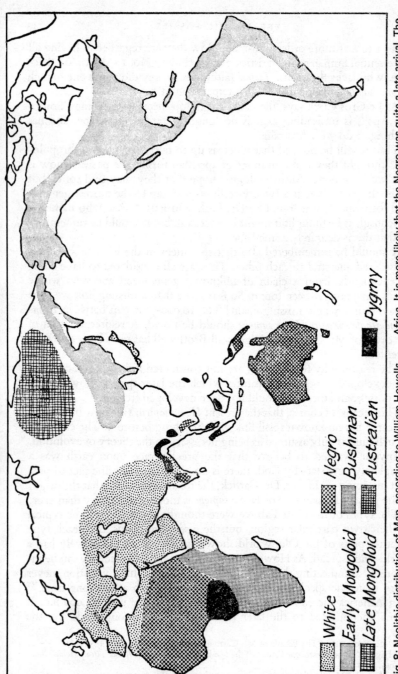

Fig. 8: Neolithic distribution of Man, according to William Howells in *Scientific American*. The only feature which might be questioned on this map of Howells' is the presence of the Negro in West Africa. It is more likely that the Negro was quite a late arrival. The Pigmy and Bushman are the originals. Howells dates this map of 8,000 B.C., but this is related to the dating systems of 1960.

White

Early Mongoloid

Late Mongoloid

Negro

Bushman

Australian

Pygmy

Indians. A problem for those who believe in the existence of an unknown common ancestor is that no tool types connected with him have been found.

If there was no such common ancestor then it means there must have been sudden jumps and creative readjustments of type development. This would not fit in comfortably with the theory of mechanistic evolution.

There are, of course, some things we cannot tell from the shape of skeletal remains, such as hair, skin colour and soft parts. Anthropometry (measurement of humans) was a branch of anthropology which has now been largely abandoned. It was a technique of measuring shapes and sizes and building up theories on this morphology.

For example, it was suggested that our three[10] main branches of the present human race of *Homo sapiens* were derived from three facial shapes of skulls of *Homo sapiens* (Aurignacians) which appeared 30,000 years ago in late Old Stone Age times. They were:

The Cro-Magnon type whose skull shape was thought to be typically "European".

The Chancelade type who were thought to be Mongolian or Asiatic in appearance.

The Grimaldi type whose prominent jaw and other shapes were thought Negroid.

It is now thought that such polymorphism, even if limited to three kinds, is of more recent origin, otherwise differences would have been greater throughout our present species. Some anthropologists put this divergence from our ancestral stock of *Homo sapiens*, as recent as 6,000 years ago.

It has been asked whether previous "human" creatures were wiped out by successive catastrophes, such as ice ages or flood, and suggested that the Noahic Flood was another such threat of annihilation. This may well be. Even many millions of years before the appearance of human types, the fossil record of animals indicates wide-scale destruction by flood as in the Ludlow fish-bone-bed in the Palaeozoic, and there have been various species which have come to a sudden universal end. In the human era *Homo neanderthalensis* disappeared universally, and 10,000 years seem to have passed before modern *Homo sapiens* came upon the scene.

Also a break 11,000 years ago revealed in the caves of Europe and the Near East indicate a fresh start for Adam's culture (see the author's "In Search of Cain").

The Christian's interest will be whether these pre-adamic men were fallen or unfallen, whether they had a conscience, a soul and a sense of

[10] Many anthropologists think now that there are four or five basic variations or polymorphisms.

religion. These questions are rather much to ask from fossils! Nevertheless, there are some guides:

Homo neanderthalensis[11] buried his dead with ceremony, which might indicate a belief in an after-life, and therefore, perhaps, a belief in soul or spirit and other aspects which go with these things.

We note that in Genesis 1 God did give instructions to Old Stone Age man, but there was no forbidden tree (Gen. 1:29). So perhaps conscience was not fully possessed. It is thought, however, that among some *homos* there was savagery and cannibalism, but not among others.

As Ezekiel shows that Satan's Fall was early in creation in a mineral-logical era, it is possible that he had caused earlier races to fall Ezek. 28:13; under the analogy of Tyrus (cf. John 8:44).

[11] E. K. Victor Pearce, *Origin of Man*, Falcon, London 1967, p. 12. Proto-neolithic Adam and Recent Anthropology, *Journal Amer. Scientific Aff.* Vol. 23, 4. Dec. 1971 pp. 130–139.

CHAPTER V

DID ADAM START THE REVOLUTION?

FOR MANY YEARS PREHISTORIC ARCHAEOLOGISTS HAD SOUGHT TO unravel the puzzle of where and how man had learned his horticulture. What had sparked off this sudden advance called the New Stone Age Revolution? From what source had he received his seed grain? In what locality or "nuclear area" had the first experiments commenced? Concerning the last question each prehistorian favoured his pet area. The name "Prehistorian" is one used to combine anthropology with archaeology. Gordon Childe was one of the greatest prehistorians, but he was also an aggressive atheist. Gordon Childe[1] wished to think that the agricultural revolution had commenced in Europe; then he shifted his attention to Egypt. As more evidence came in, the search was taken to the Fertile Crescent of the Near East. Then Braidwood[2] at a hint from Seton Lloyd investigated Jarmo village in the Iranian foothills. Meanwhile Kathleen Kenyon was excavating the city of Jericho[3] down to the earliest New Stone Age and beyond.

Although farming in its early stages was present in these areas it was realized that the original culture area was still to be found. Then James Mellaart discovered that Great New Stone Age city, Catal Hüyük, on the Turkish Plateau, 5,000 ft. up, far above the foothills, with its evidence of early farming. From the depth of excavations, so far, its archaeological history already stretches back to eight millennia B.C. and terminated 5000 B.C. In this Neolithic city were the evidences that farming in the market gardens around was already well advanced.

Braidwood's Jarmo village in the foothills 700 miles to the East, was now seen to be only a receiving area. Dr. Seton Lloyd, who is a great authority on Middle East archaeology, discovered Jarmo when riding on horseback, and drew Braidwood's attention to it, but he always felt it would prove to be no more than a receiving area.

What has become evident is that the Bible was right in speaking about New Stone Age cities so soon after Adam's farming revolution. Until recently it was thought that social organization was insufficiently advanced for cities to be supported and organized in the New Stone Age. The first urbanization was thought to have commenced in Mesopotamia in the early Bronze Age, 4000 B.C., and then to have spread to Egypt.

[1] Gordon Childe, *The Prehistory of European Soc.* (Pelican, 1958).
[2] R. J. Braidwood, *Nr. East and the Foundations for Civilization* (University of Oregon Press, 1961).
[3] K. Kenyon, *Digging up Jericho* (Benn, 1957).

At the time when the earlier theory was prevalent I had written in the margin of my RSV Bible against Gen. 4:17 the exclamation "A New Stone Age city!" The text read, "And Cain built a city and he called the name of the city after the name of his son Enoch." We observed earlier that the New Stone Age was referred to because the discovery of metals comes later in the Text. The discovery of metals was made by Tubal-cain (Gen. 4:22). He must have discovered the rich copper and iron ores in that area, for we know that native copper and iron were used later at Catal Hüyük by 6000 B.C. This was before the days of smelting in the Bronze Age of 4000 B.C. The copper was beaten out cold, and so was the iron ore. This iron ore was haematite containing 70 per cent iron, the richest ore obtainable, but because it was so tough to beat out without the knowledge of iron smelting, it soon fell out of use, and had to await the advent of the great Hittite smelters c.1500 B.C. in this same area of Asia Minor (Josh. 17: 19 and 3:10).

Through lack of knowledge of New Stone Age cities, and of the use of native iron as early as 6000 B.C., Dr. David Dye was at a disadvantage in his attempts to identify the era, and wrong in his remark that we need not take the Bible references to Stone Age cities too seriously. Archaeologists have found before that even the small details of the text of Holy Scripture give valuable clues to impending discoveries. Apart from this criticism, his book *Faith and the Physical World* on general science is excellent.[4]

When that remark was being written in the margin of my Bible, Prof. James Mellaart had actually begun to excavate one of those New Stone Age cities near the area described in that Scripture. He startled the archaeological world by his articles. One appeared in the *Scientific American*, 1964, headed "A Neolithic City in Turkey."[5]

It was no mean city either – far bigger than Jericho, it covered 23 acres, and showed specialization of trades, indicating a large market gardening area of villages to support the inhabitants. "Catal Hüyük deserves the name of city: it was a community with an extensive economic development, specialized crafts, a rich religious life, a surprising attainment in art and an impressive social organization."

It was the centre of a volcanic glass trade which ranged far afield, even to Jericho and other trade centres. Weaving and pattern-dyeing were also practised. Mellaart wrote, "One cannot possibly be wrong in suggesting that it was a well-organized trade that produced the city's wealth. Moreover, it appears likely that the trade in obsidian was at the heart of this extensive commerce. This black volcanic glass, which first appeared in the preceding Mesolithic period, became the most widespread trading commodity during the Neolithic period in the Near East. It has been found

⁴ D. Dye, *Faith and the Physical World* (Paternoster P., 1966), p. 152.
⁵ Other works by J. Mellaart are: *Anatolia*, Cambridge Ancient History (CUP, 1964), and *Catal Hüyük* (Thames & Hudson, 1967).

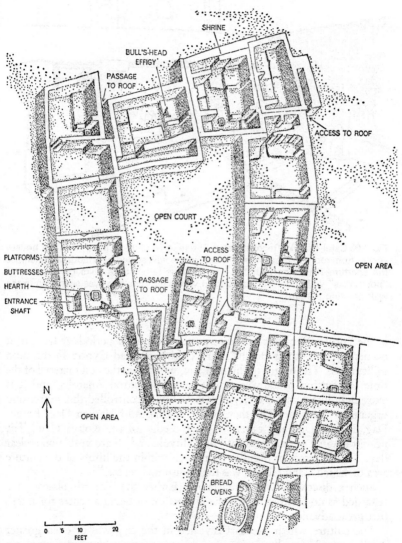

Fig. 9: Catal Hüyük: 5th Layer. Community Arrangements of 8,000 years ago in the Neolithic City, S. Turkey. Lower layers are much older than this. Note the access by ladders to the roof, from which all houses were entered.

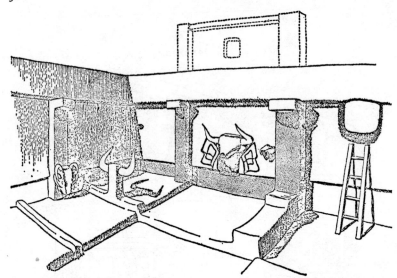

Fig. 10: Catal Hüyük: Reconstructed Shrine in Neolithic City. Within the houses access from room to room was by a hole in the wall scaled by a ladder. Sometimes the aperture would be near the floor. This is rather a cavelike conception, as "pot-holers" will know. An association with cave-dwelling was seen also in the wall-painting patterns.

in the "proto-Neolithic" and pre-pottery Neolithic periods at Jericho; it occurs as far south as Beidha near Petra: it reached Cyprus in the sixth millennium. The origin of this obsidian, which was the best material of the time for cutting tools, was almost certainly central Anatolia, and it is extremely likely that the city of Catal Hüyük controlled this source and organized the trade. The then active volcanoes of Hasban Dag, Karaca Dag, Mekke Dag and others lie on the edge of the Konya Plain. The nearest is some 50 miles east of Catal Hüyük, and all are visible on a clear day. These sources of obsidian were well within the limits of the culture area of which Catal Hüyük was the undisputed centre."[6]

Such a discovery was a revelation. Earlier the Turkish plateau was regarded as no competitor for the distinction of being a centre for man's first great advance.

The culture which Mellaart revealed in the city was of even greater significance. The wall paintings and design of the city showed connexions with former cave dwellers, for there were unmistakable similarities with those famous cave paintings around the Mediterranean and in the Sahara. Although the city was so elaborate, they did not enter rooms through

[6] J. Mellaart, "A Neolithic City in Turkey", *Scientific American*, April, 1964, p. 94.

doors but through holes in the wall! A rather cave-like conception. There were no streets. The dwellers walked over the flat roofs, for there were no alleys between the houses and sanctuaries. To traverse the city one climbed a ladder, walked across the roofs, and disappeared through a hole down a ladder into the desired house. It is interesting to know that the Pueblo maize-growing Indians have similar villages with roof-top access.[7] Also they practise dry farming similar to that described in Genesis 2 (flood water seeps through porous strata to the crops).

It seemed to be a peaceful community. Throughout the earlier centuries of its long history there were no signs of warfare. Although it was a very religious community, its offerings seemed to be Cain-like offerings of cereals without resort to animal sacrifices.

The beginnings of agriculture and sheep-farming started while men were still in caves. This is shown through the Neolithic cave of Shanidar where an increasing percentage of sheep were firstlings.[8] As well as proving that breeding was taking place it also implied the use of lamb sacrifices, for we read that Abel brought some of the firstlings of his flock for sacrifice to the Lord God as an atonement for his sins. It was Cain's refusal to bring a sin-offering which caused his rejection (Gen. 4:7).

We need not suppose that Catal Hüyük is the actual city Cain built. Mellaart thinks we shall be finding other Stone Age cities built farther east along this high plateau.

We do not know whether Adam was sophisticated enough to build cities. It is unlikely, as his descendants, Cain and his son, were given the credit for this. So that Adam's initiation of farming would be in the proto-Neolithic stage when early farmers still lived in caves and rock shelters, like the Natufians.

Mellaart says that the core of the mound remains to be sounded, and may take the origins of Catal Hüyük back to the end of the last continental glaciation (Ice Age).

It was at the termination of the Ice Age that farming developed. Prehistorians used to suggest that it was the post-glacial conditions which gave man the idea of farming. At the retreat of the ice caps on the Caucasian range and Ararat ranges in Turkey, a sparse tundra vegetation would be left which would later be succeeded by birch and pine wood. Meanwhile melting ice would keep the plateau valleys supplied with water rather than through rain which might be scarce on account of the high pressure outward-blowing wind systems.

These small isolated valleys would be virtual "Gardens of Eden", and of course one of them must have been the garden of Eden itself, because horticulture must have started in some particular plot. Or perhaps it was

[7] C. Daryll Forde, op. cit., pp. 240–2.

[8] Evidence for this is by measurement of the progress of ossification, especially in the symphyseal areas.

a region wider than one valley, for Scripture describes it as large enough to contain the sources of four rivers.

It was suggested that animals seeking water-supply would be brought into close association with men, giving him the idea of breeding animals. This was called the "Oasis" theory. It sounded plausible, but prehistorians asked why farming did not start in similar conditions before when there were retreats of ice and "inter-stadials" on various occasions earlier, and the same could be said concerning cereal development. To many it was an inadequate explanation. It would appear from the Bible that Divine-initiation was the main cause, for it was God who placed Adam in the garden to till it, and who brought the animals to Adam to see what he would name them Gen. 2:19, 20.

In the following selection of passages from Genesis it will be seen that post-glacial conditions seem to be described: "No plant of the field was yet in the earth and no herb of the field had sprung up – for the Lord God had not caused it to rain upon the earth." (Gen. 2:5, RSV). Here are the tundra vegetation and dry outward-blowing wind conditions we would expect.

Periglacial melt-water is next described: "But a flood (not mist) went up from the earth and watered the whole face of the ground." (Gen. 2:6). The location was at the sources of four rivers supplied by glacial melt-water: "A river flowed out of Eden to water the garden, and there it divided and became four rivers. (Lord Kinross describes their common source). The name of the first is Pison. . . . The name of the second river is Gihon (probably Araxes). It flows around the whole land of Cush. . . . The name of the third river is Tigris which flows east of Assyria (Iraq), and the fourth river is the Euphrates" (which flows from Turkey to the Persian Gulf) (see Gen. 2:10–14). The Bible is thus correct about the place of origin of farming. There is no uncertainty about the identity of the rivers Tigris and Euphrates, whose headwaters rise in Turkey.

The following analysis of the Hebrew text published fifteen years before the discoveries concerning the Turkish Steppe Plateau supports this exposition. It is from the New Bible Handbook of 1947:[9] "The Eden of Genesis 2 is probably the same word as the Babylonian "Edinnu", which denotes a plateau or steppe. . . . The land which lies east of the upper reaches of the Tigris was known by the Kassites as Cush, which implies that the Gihon was the Araxes and that Eden was in the region assigned to it by Sumerian tradition, at the headwaters of the great rivers of Mesopotamia." The cool evenings mentioned in Genesis 3:8, would be typical of the high plateau.

The following verses of chapter 2 clearly speak of the initiation of the New Stone Age Farming Revolution: "There was no man to till the ground" (Gen. 2:5). "And the Lord God planted a garden in Eden, in the

⁹ G. T. Manley, *The New Bible Handbook* (IVF, 1947), p. 82.

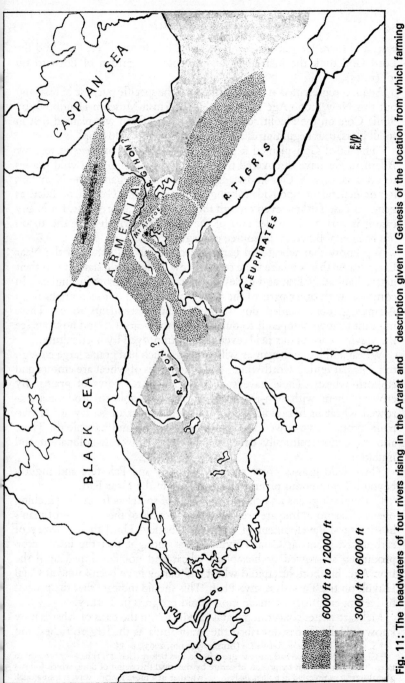

Fig. 11: The headwaters of four rivers rising in the Ararat and Armenian mountain ranges which would appear to answer the description given in Genesis of the location from which farming spread.

east; and there He put the man whom he had formed" (v. 8). "And the Lord God took the man and put him into the garden of Eden to till it" (v. 15).

Adam is represented as being formed for the specific purpose of carrying out this New Stone Age gardening. The British Museum Handbook by Sonia Cole on the Neolithic Revolution says, "Corn was planted first in small plots, thus beginning as a garden rather than a field crop".[10]

"The Lord God planted a garden".[11] The words are a clue to how Adam might have discovered the secret of cross-pollinating wild grasses to produce cereals. Our knowledge that farming began in the Near East is not dependent upon identifying the area of the Garden of Eden as being in East Turkey, even though this would appear probable, for in any case it is part of the wider area of the Near East which since the 1950's has been established as the source of farming.

We know that wheat and barley first became cultivated in the Near East because that is where these cereals grew in their wild state. It was their native habitat. Wheat and barley did not originally grow in England. In common with other parts of the world we received our seed grains from Adam's garden, handed down through his descendants to us. These migrant farmers shipped it to our Islands 3400 years B.C. and now we see the waving corn in our fields even further improved by horticulture.

Wheat and barley began as wild grasses which had grains large enough to make harvesting worthwhile. The wild forms of wheat are emmer and einkorn wheats. These have two rows and three rows of grains. By crossing them with two-rowed grass man was able to produce a six-rowed wheat or hexaploid wheat. The wild forms of barley are in two main groups, two-rowed and six-rowed (diploid and hexaploid). These also were horticulturally developed by man by cross-pollination and mutation.

These wild grasses grow native in Turkey and Palestine and slightly beyond. Leguminous plants also originated in the Near East.

Carbonized grains and clay impressions of spikelets from the parching ovens of Jarmo in Iraq are archaeological records of the progress of man's horticultural development of wheat and barley. Until the discovery of carbonized grains at Catal Hüyük it was thought that the heavy crop producing six-rowed or hexaploid wheat had not developed until the Iron Age, but both hexaploid wheat and barley have been found at Catal Hüyük on the Turkish Konya Plain. This should indicate that the process had a longer history or made more rapid progress in Turkey.

Mellaart writes concerning Catal Hüyük: "On the basis of what is now known, Helbaek has described the grain finds as the largest, richest and

[10] S. Cole, *The Neolithic Revolution* (British Museum, 1963), p. 13.

[11] Gen. 2:8. What God had made to grow in the ages before (Gen. 1:11) he now brought to Eden. Whether this was by process of nature by the usual succession of flora, which follows glacial retreat as revealed in pollen analysis, or whether in a more specific way, is immaterial.

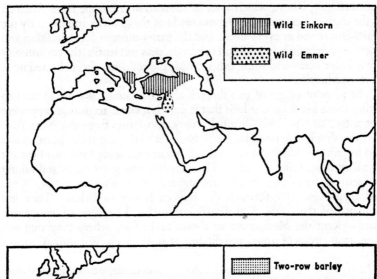

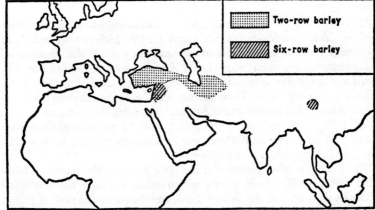

Fig. 12: Maps of Native cereals, according to S. Cole of the British Museum, showing where barley and wheat originally grew wild.
(*above*): The distribution of wild wheat
(*below*): The distribution of wild barley.
The carbohydrate-yielding cereals are native to areas where protein-rich leguminous plants, or pulses, also grow wild. Oil-producing plants, such as flax, were also important, and various roots and fruit were cultivated in Neolithic times as well.

best preserved of all early cereal deposits so far recovered, providing some of the most significant genetical and cultural data yet obtained about early civilization. The grains, unlike the finds in other early Near Eastern settlements of cultivated plants little removed from their wild ancestors, include such hybrids and mutants as naked six-row barley and hexaploid free-threshing wheat, which were introduced into Europe from Anatolia in the sixth millenium B.C. The use made of the grains is indicated by the grain-bins found in every house and the many mortars for dehusking and querns for grinding. In addition to cereals, peas and lentils, the community grew bitter vetch and some other crops; the residents also collected nuts, fruits and berries."[12]

The place of origin of our sheep is also fascinating. We are so used to seeing them graze on our hills that it does not occur to us that they were not native to our land. Originally they, too, came from the Near East. Farmers slowly migrated from the Near East bringing their sheep, grains and techniques. Many came overland, but our seafaring forebears brought them by boat, tying the sheep's legs together by grass ropes and sailing and settling, first along the Mediterranean coasts, farther and farther West, and then eventually through the Bay of Biscay to Britain. They left evidence of the route of their migrations by their style of megalithic tombs along the Mediterranean shores to Britain, where they dug out their great circles of stones and ditches, as at Avebury, Wiltshire (Gen. 10: 4, 5).

Many other crops were also developed, and cattle, goats and pigs were bred in Eden's garden-farms. Of Catal Hüyük Mellaart writes: "The zoological remains are no less interesting: they show the presence of domesticated sheep even below Level X and cows as early as Level VII. Goats and dogs also appear to have been domesticated, but there is no indication that pigs were. Their absence may be due to religious consider-ations. Although the domesticated animals provided the community with wool, milk, meat and skins, the people had by no means abandoned hunting. Wild cattle and red deer were extensively hunted, as were wild asses, wild sheep, boars and leopards."[13]

There are also other proofs that the Near East was the source of Neo-lithic farming. We have briefly given what is called the biological evidence, namely, that the animals bred, and the particular type of grasses cultivated, were native to that area. The biological evidence also includes the examination of animal bones. As sheep and goats became more and more selectively bred, the twisted horn-cores of the wild types became straighter. Burnt corn left in the ovens of Jarmo showed how better ears of corn developed.

Two other lines of evidence combine to prove that the Near East was the focal area, i.e., the archaeological evidence and that of radio-carbon dating.

Archaeology is now a very exact science. Sites are dug out according to strict rules. The lower down through the layers one digs, the earlier are the styles of pottery, building and tools. Rubbish left in caves, and

---

[12] J. Mellaart, op. cit.
[13] Ibid.

also on city mounds is valuable evidence. Fortunately (for us!), there were no City Corporation dustmen in those days. Rubbish was just thrown out, old walls flattened down, and new houses built on top of the rubbish. Eventually, the latest city and defence walls were built on quite a high mound, a man-made hill, with perhaps 6,000 years of history beneath it.[14]

The cultural sequence extends back furthest of all in the Near East, and particularly in Turkey, Mesopotamia, and Palestine.

The migrating farmers made their way through Europe as the centuries and millennia passed, so that the cultural sequence of dates became more recent in ever-widening circles through the world, from the focal point of diffusion.

It is fascinating to study the various sites throughout Europe, as well as the sequence in Egypt, India and China.

Fossil pollen analysis also plays its part. It can tell us the actual succession of trees and crops which were grown in the field or clearing.

We can trace the sequence of slash-and-burn farming as New Stone Age man made his way through Europe, making clearances in the forest with his sharp-ground stone axes, and when the soil was exhausted passing on his way to make a new clearing.

One stone axe found in Denmark after 4,000 years' rest was used by archaeologists to chop down 100 birch trees!

By tracing the source of the igneous stone or flint used for such axes, we can trace their manufacture to five main factories which supplied farmers all over England.

The first "wave" of farmers worked the lighter and easier loess soils of the wooded hills of Europe, mainly following the course of the Danube; hence they are called Danubians.

The first Danubians reached Central Europe by 5000 B.C., and farmed in peace for a thousand years.

They are noted for their long log houses built of split timbers. Some of these were as long as 120 to 150 feet. They would consist of a series of single rooms with a passage running the whole length of one side, rather like some army huts. Some bear evidence of rooms being added as the family grew. The roofs were given an extremely steep pitch, to give a quick run off for the heavy rains of central Europe. This was an interesting adaptation to a cool temperate climate in contrast to the dry heat of the Mediterranean climate from which their forefathers migrated.

The origin of their culture, however, was reflected in the shape of their pots. They were of gourd shape typical of the Near East and incised with shell marks of East Mediterranean origin. This also showed that they were in trade contact with the Mediterranean.

They farmed in peace for a thousand years, on the slash-and-burn

[14] Seton Lloyd, *Mounds of the Near East*, Edin. Univ. Press, 1958.

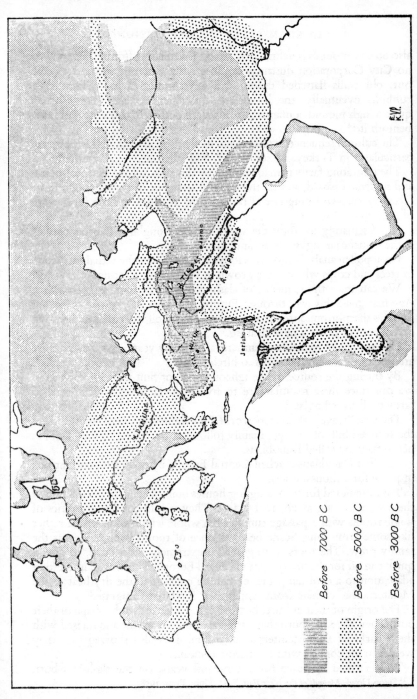

Fig. 12: The Spread of Neolithic Farming from the plateau lands and new fold mountains of the Near East

Before 7000 B C

Before 5000 B C

Before 3000 B C

R. EUPHRATES

R. TIGRIS

CAUCASUS

ZAGROS

Jericho

E.W.
K.

system. First they would make a clearing in the dense European forest of that time, and plant their crops in the virgin soil, but after ten years the weeds which so cursed the Garden of Eden could be held back no longer, and as the soil became exhausted, they would move to their new clearing. This would leave the old clearing to secondary growth, the evidence of which archaeologists of our time have been able to detect by pollen analysis.

The life led by the farmers of Borneo may be a good picture of that of the first Danubians. They live in long rectangular wooden houses built on stilts. Each long-house is divided into units for a single family which is a member of the greater family occupying the whole erection.

Every ten years they pull down the erection and move on to virgin forest. They clear the new area by chopping down the trees whose ashes they burn to enrich the soil for the crops to follow. This is typical slash-and-burn farming. The method causes soil erosion eventually and loss of good agricultural land, for once vegetation is removed torrential rains create gullies and wash away the soil.

In South-East Europe the first farmers reached the Balkans over a thousand years before the first Danubians reached the central European loess hills, being nearer to the dispersal area of Turkey and Iran. This was from 7000 to 6000 B.C. Their adaptation to the long deep valleys of Greece was to build round wattle huts on a stone base. Later they found that houses of square shape better suited their needs.

It is astonishing to reflect that in these early times, 5000 B.C., New Stone Age farmers sailed the length of the Mediterranean bringing with them their cattle, sheep and pigs. They would land to graze their domesticated animals as they migrated farther and farther along the Northern shores of the Mediterranean. Their assemblage of implements was of the simplest. Indeed they are noted only for possessing soup ladles and ear plugs! One can only imagine why the ear plugs were necessary. Perhaps their beat groups drummed far into the night!

Archaeologists had already worked out the dates for these peoples, and so when radio-carbon dating was invented by Libby in 1958, it provided an independent witness. The radio-carbon tests on the bones and crafts at the various sites gave the same picture of an ever-widening circle of migration throughout the world from the focal centre. Renfrew admits that the small revision of C. 14 by bristlecone-pine dating does not alter this general picture of diffusion (*Before Civilization*, pp. 143, 167).

The South East Pacific was still of New Stone Age Culture until recently. It reached Melanesia 6,000 B.C., but the Maoris occupied New Zealand only one thousand years ago.

In contrast, the old land bridge at the Bering Straits brought farming early to America. The earliest maize growing in America is dated by radio-carbon as 3,650 B.C., from Bat Cave, New Mexico, comparatively

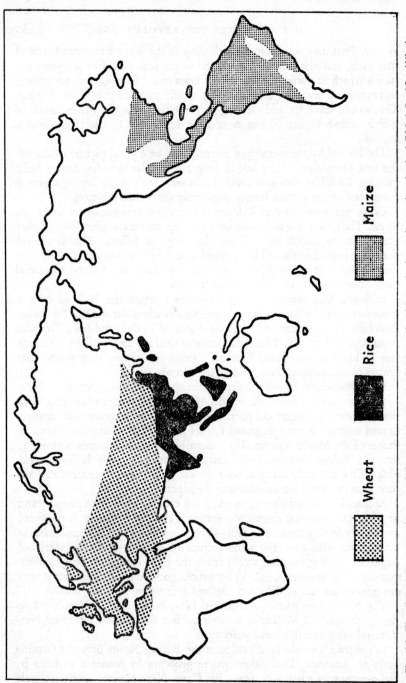

Fig. 14: The three great cereal areas of the world: the distribution of cultivated wheat, rice and maize in 1,500 A.D. *After Wissler*

Wheat   Rice   Maize

near the Pueblo maize growers. In South America dates around 2,500 B.C. have been obtained.

Maize was not the earliest plant to be cultivated in the New World, however. Gourds, lima beans and squashes came before it. The symposium published in 1969 by world specialists on "The Domestication and Exploitation of Plants and Animals"[15] says that the first plants to be cultivated in the New World are dated by radio-carbon as 6,500 B.C.[16] This was the American bean, *Phaseolus*, in Mexico.

The great question is how did cultivation arise in America? Did it commence as an independent revolution, or did it come via Asia from the Middle East? If the latter, then why was not the staple crop originally wheat instead of maize?

C. D. Darlington of the Botany School, Oxford, and contributor to the above symposium, considers that cultivators moving from old areas to new ones adopted new crops as they moved. Wheat was replaced by its own weeds, rye, oats and buckwheat in the northern regions, and in the southern regions by its own millet.

Gradually in India the division into three regions depending on wheat, rice and sorghum has been stabilized.[17]

In East Asia pottery associated with the third Neolithic stage had reached Japan six millennia B.C.

In China, reaping knives showed that wheat had preceded rice seven millennia B.C. according to Wm. Watson of the symposium (p. 397): "The knives occur in a full Neolithic context, or on sites where grain has been recovered ... These knives are distributed mainly along the middle course of the Yellow River, to the North-east as far as Liaotung." The long journeys by caravan through the Gobi Desert, was an ancient means of rapid transference of culture between Western Asia and East Asia from whence the New World Early Mongoloids came.

There are Americans who prefer to think that an independent Neolithic revolution started in the New World. But Darlington states that this view follows from Vavilov's theory of crop origins 1926. Subsequent investigation reveals, however, that Vavilov's centres of diversity were not so much primary as secondary – not so much the sites of origin as places of development.[18] Indeed, Grahame Clark of Cambridge points out that the North American Neolithic bone handles, slotted to receive flint flakes, have their origin in northern Eurasia.[19] Perhaps the similarities between the American Pueblo culture and Catal Hüyük indicate an

[15] Ucko and Dimbleby, *The Domestication and Exploitation of Plants and Animals*. Duckworth, London, 1969.

[16] B. Pickersgill, "The Domestication of Chili peppers in Ucko and Dimbleby", op. cit., p. 443 and J. Smartt p. 452.

[17] Ucko and Dimbleby, "Patterns of Exploitation" op. cit., p. 68.

[18] Ibid., p. 67.

[19] Grahame Clark, *World Prehistory*, Cambridge 1962, pp. 195, 210.

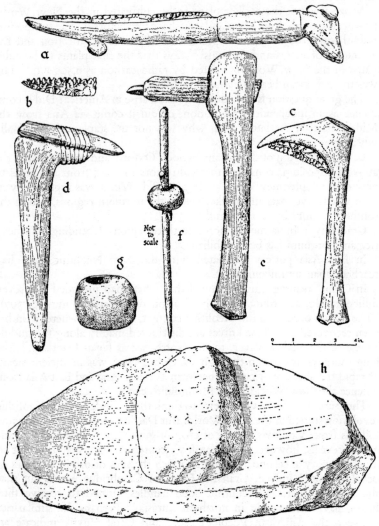

Fig. 15: The Tools Adam used may have been like these (one-fifth size): (a) Goat-headed antler sickle with flint teeth restored; Natufian. *After Curwen*; (b) Flint saw-blade; (c) Crescentic flint sickle-blade in an antler haft. (d) "Neolithic" hoe (or adze) with polished stone head; (e) Pick; (f) Digging stick with stone weight; (g) Quern and rubbing-stone for grinding wheat.

ancestry in Turkey which reach America via the Bering Straits from East Asia.

Some take it for granted that when New Stone Age man migrated he intermarried with the earlier Stone Age peoples, and indeed this could be inferred concerning Cain and his wife, or it could be a possible explanation of the intermarriage referred to in Genesis 6 between the "sons of God" (the Adamic race) and the "daughters of men" (surviving members of earlier creations). But this would not make Eve "the mother of all living". That there is no genetic connection between Adamites and former races gains support from the remarkable emptiness of the lands into which the migrating farmers came. The first Danubians feared no attack from any earlier inhabitants of Europe. Had they disappeared? Likewise, Africa seemed to be empty in the West, Central and Southern areas, according to their ethnological history until very late. The Bushmen are an exception, but like the Australian Aborigines they were probably an early Neolithic migration which became isolated. Melanesian tradition depicts their ancestors as entering empty lands. In Northern Europe the axes of the Mesolithic migrants reveal a connection with the early Natufian farmer-hunters of the Near East. They arrived with the knowledge of farming but reverted to secondary hunter-gathering.

The archaeological break (hiatus) before the Mesolithic or Natufian seems widely general in cave stratigraphy. This would indicate that the Adamic race was a fresh start eleven thousand years ago.[20]

Thus to all parts of the World the new revolutionary mode of subsistence was diffused. Farmers moving east, west, north and south brought their techniques, and even their animals, from the area described as the Garden of Eden, where Adam was made in order to farm.

It seems, therefore, a reasonable inference, by correlating science with Scripture, that Adam under God's direction started this New Stone Age Revolution.

It answers the prehistorian's enigma on what could have caused this momentous long-awaited advance.

[20] E. K. Victor Pearce, "Proto-neolithic Adam", *J. Amer. Scient.*, *AFF.*, Vol. 23, 4. Dec. 1971, pp. 130–9.

CHAPTER VI

THE ORIGIN OF RELIGION

O NE OF THE PRIME FACTS OF THE SCIENCE OF MAN IS HIS ASTONISHING worldwide need for religion. Whether we think him misguided or otherwise in this, does not alter the fact. Neither does man's misuse of religion.

Is religion an instinct implanted by God for a purpose because the Creator is an objective reality? The second and third chapters of Genesis give sense to this inherent characteristic, by showing that man was intended to commune and walk with God.

Professor Evans-Pritchard, Head of the Institute of Social Anthropology, Oxford, was a pioneer in a number of questions. He maintained that if the world views of primitive peoples were investigated carefully there would be found a belief in a supreme God-Creator.

Older anthropologists were deceived by the fact that primitive peoples' religion is taken up with placating the lesser gods and spirits, many of which were considered evil. They had also to placate ancestral spirits and nature spirits. When pressed to explain why they rarely mention the High God, they might reply that it was not necessary to concern themselves with him as he never did them any harm. Other anthropologists, taking this lead from Evans-Pritchard, have confirmed this claim of an early belief in one supreme Creator.

Robert Nassau lived forty years among the Ainu, who are the original inhabitants of Japan, and said, "If suddenly they should be asked the flat question, 'Do you know Anyambe (the Creator)?' they would probably tell any white visitor, trader, traveller, or even missionary, under a feeling of their general ignorance and white man's superior knowledge, 'No! What do *we* know? You are white people and are spirits; you come from Njambi's town, and know all about him!' (This will help to explain what is probably true, that some natives have sometimes made the thoughtless admission that they 'know nothing about a God'). I reply, 'No, I am not a spirit; and while I do know about Anyambe, I do not call him by that name. It's your word. Where did you get it?' 'Our forefathers told us that name. Njambe is the One-who-made-us. He is our Father'. Pursuing the conversation, they will interestedly and voluntarily say, 'He made these trees, that mountain, this river, these goats and chickens, and us people'."[1]

Dr. Wilhelm Schmidt of Vienna compiled his monumental work on primitive Monotheism.[2] He collected from all over the world these

[1] S. M. Zwemer, *Origin of Religion* (MMS, 1935).
[2] W. Schmidt, *Origin and Growth of Religion* (Vienna).

beliefs of the original native stocks, present before any missionary influence was brought to bear. Did such knowledge of the Supreme Creator come through Adam? Or was the knowledge a later product *. er millennia of painful groping through lower forms of religion and fear of the forces of nature?

Earlier social anthropologists were prone to give inadequate theories for the origin of man's universal sense of religion. Victorian writers such as Frazer who wrote *The Golden Bough*,[3] and Tylor,[4] followed by Durkheim, Levy Bruhl, etc., all thought up individual explanations for the origin of it. According to one theory it evolved from magic and religion to science. Another was that it came *via* shadows, spirits and gods, or dreams, spirits, polytheism and monotheism. These were all subjective theories, thought-conditioned by the mode of life enjoyed by the upper class of Victorian England. This fashion of reasoning was based upon whether an argument sounded convincing to Western ears without a search for facts, and was called dialectical analysis.[5] It was bound to pass away with the advent of empirical inductive analysis of field research among the people they speculated upon. Since then there has been a great advance in ethnological knowledge. Professor Evans-Pritchard and others declared that the above-mentioned Victorians never had field experience of primitive peoples, or only a superficial one. Baker said of the Nuer that they were without belief in a Supreme Being. Evans-Pritchard went to live among them and found that this was not true. Likewise Dr. A. Butt found belief in a Supreme Being in British Guiana. This supports the findings of such as Schmidt, Lang and Zwemer, who found that original beliefs all over the world were in a Supreme Being often called the Sky God or High God. They thought this indicated that God revealed himself to earlier peoples who had handed it down to present day primitives. Polytheism came later as a corruption of the original purer revelation.

It was the pioneer Andrew Lang who first claimed that there had been no evolution of religion, but rather a degeneration. He said: "Man being what he is, was certain to 'go a-whoring' after practically useful ghosts, ghost-gods, and fetishes which he could keep in his wallet or 'medicine bag'. For these he was sure, in the long run, first to neglect his idea of his Creator; next, perhaps, to reckon him as only one, if the

[3] Sir J. Frazer, *The Golden Bough* (abridged edition, London, 1922).

[4] Sir Edward Tylor, *Anthropology* (London, 1881).

[5] It would seem that we now have to add the recent theory of Desmond Morris (*The Naked Ape*, Cape, London, 1967), to this list of Victorian-styled reasoning. He appears to be unaware of the Victorian attempts to account for religion, or of the social anthropologists' abandonment of plausibility in favour of inductive analysis. He suggests that reverence in religion comes from the sexual subjection in monkeys to dominance! As Lewis & Towers point out (in *Naked Ape or Homo Sapiens,* Garnstone, London, 1969), Hominids are *not* lineally descended from monkeys or apes and the question of inheritance of behavioural patterns is therefore irrelevant. John Allegro's mushroom fantasy is yet another example (1970). Scholars have already declared it unfounded on fact or philology.

highest, of the venerable rabble of spirits or deities, and to sacrifice to him, as to them. And this is exactly what happened! If we are not to call it 'degeneration', what are we to call it?"[5]

This is the order given in the Bible also, which Wellhausen completely rehashed and juggled around to give this Victorian idea of a man-made evolution of religion.

Among the last primitive tribes to be discovered are the Kapauku Papuans of New Guinea. In their mountain fastnesses cut off from the rest of the world, of which they were unaware, they continued in their New Stone Age culture. This indicates that they originate from the first migration of New Stone Age farmers, as later Bronze Age tools are unknown by them.

Dr. Pospisil first studied them in 1954-55. The Kapauku were a society still in its pristine aboriginal state, and, he says, "dramatically contradicts the preconceived ideas and clichés addressed by the West to primitive peoples in general".

Reporting their "World View", Dr. Pospisil says, "The universe itself and all existence was *ebijata*, 'designed by *Ugatame*', the Creator. *Ugatame* has a dual nature: he is supposed to be masculine and feminine at the same time, is referred to as the two entities, and is manifested to the people by the duality of the sun and the moon. To my inquiry whether *Ugatame was* the sun and the moon I received as an answer a firm denial. Sun is conceived as a ball of fire, because it provides light and is warm; moon is believed to be a cold light like that of a firefly or the bacteria that infest rotting wood. Sun and moon are only manifestations of *Ugatame* who thus makes his presence known to the people. They definitely are *not* the Creator himself. To make the matters more complex, in the old days the people did not even have a single term for this deity. They referred to him as "sun and moon, they two". The concept of the Creator is an old one, as evidenced by its use in many prayers and magical rites in 1954."[6]

This Stone Age tribe was not without its abstract philosophy as the following shows so intriguingly: "*Ugatame* is omniscient, omnipotent, and omnipresent, credited with the creation of all things and with having determined all events. Strangely enough, however, he is believed not to exist himself. When I questioned this contention, a Kapauku defended it skilfully by a question: "But how can he exist when he created all the existence?" Obviously *Ugatame* is beyond existence, because to the Kapauku all that exists must be of phenomenal nature; one must be able either to see, hear, smell, taste, or feel it. But the Creator is beyond this phenomenal dimension, because of the simple reason that he created it. Because he is, so to speak, in the fifth dimension and is not of phenomenal nature, he is able to be omnipresent."

[5] Andrew Lang, *The Making of Religion* (London, 1895), pp. 281, 282.
[6] Leo Pospisil, *The Kapauka Papuans* (Holt, Rinehart & Winston, 1963), p. 84.

It is amusing to note that they considered Westerners to be stupid in their beliefs: "A very old man from the Mapia region, supported by his two sons, managed to come to see me in the Kamu Valley. As he explained to me, his main purpose in coming was a problem he wanted to have clarified before he died. The problem concerned the white man. He could not understand how it was possible that the white man could be so clever and ingenious in designing such amazing contrivances as aeroplanes (which the old man could see flying over his valley), guns, medicines, clothes, and steel tools, and at the same time could be so primitive and illogical in his religion. 'How can you think,' he argued, 'that a man can sin and can have a free will, and at the same time believe that your God is omnipotent, and that he created the world and determined all the happenings? If he determined all that happens, and (therefore) also the bad deeds, how can a man be held responsible? Why, if he is omnipotent, did the Creator have to change himself into a man and allow himself to be killed (crucified) when it would have been enough for him just to order men to behave?' The notion that anything can be absolutely bad or good was quite incomprehensible to him. Furthermore, the Christian notion of man resembling God in appearance appeared to him as utterly primitive (*tabe-tabe*, 'stupid')."[7]

So we see that it was not only of the learned Greeks that Paul could write, "We preach Christ crucified, unto the Jews a stumbling-block, and unto the Greeks foolishness, for the preaching of the cross is to them that perish foolishness, but unto us which are saved it is the power of God" (I Cor. 1:18, 23).

Examples of this original and primitive belief in the High God or Great Spirit or Creator, can be quoted from all over the world. I will give only a few examples. James Welsh, another anthropologist, gives the following world view of the Isokos of the Niger Delta: "Their religion begins with the Supreme Being called *Oghene*, who is believed to have created the whole world and all peoples, including the Isokos. He lives in the sky which is a part of him, sends rain and sunshine, and shows his anger through thunder. *Oghene* is entirely beyond human comprehension, has never been seen, is sexless, and is only known by his actions, which have led men to speak of *Oghene* as 'him', because he is thought of as the creator and therefore father of all the Isokos. He is spoken of as Our Father, never as My Father. *Oghene* always punishes evil and rewards good."

The Indians of America are descended from the original Early Mongoloid immigrants to that continent (see p. 61 and Fig. 8). They came via the Aleutian Islands and Bering Straits of the North Pacific. Their devotion to the Great Spirit is well known. Dr. Zwemer quotes John Tanner, who was taken captive by the Indians in 1830, on how the Ottawa

[7] Ibid., p. 85.

Indians prayed to the Great Spirit before beginning their hazardous voyage:

" 'We were passed on,' he writes, 'into the sea about 200 yards, when all the boats halted together, and the chief with a very loud voice addressed a prayer to the Great Spirit, in which he implored him to conduct us safely through the sea. He said, "Thou hast made this sea, and Thou hast made us Thy children. Thou canst also arrange that the sea remains smooth, whilst we pass on in safety." In this manner he continued to pray through five or ten minutes. Then he threw into the sea a small handful of tobacco, and all of the canoes followed him. They then all continued their voyage, and the old chief began a song of a religious nature.' "[8]

Professor Daryll Forde, Head of the Department of Anthropology in London University, speaks of the conception of Supreme God, or High God, as being in a different category from earth gods. "The Creator-God concept is widespread, though attributes and doctrines vary from people to people. There is a strong identification with the sky and sun. There is a definite conception of God-Creator who is the source of life of all living things."[9]

When Professor Wilhelm Schmidt had finished his great work on "The Origin of the Idea of God", he visited Princetown Theological Seminary, and Dr. Zwemer reported the conclusion of his lecture as follows: "If we turn, as seems quite natural, first to primitive men themselves, the reply they give leads always in the direction that they have not acquired religion by their own thinking and research, but by oral tradition from their fathers and forefathers, and finally from the Creator. Among the oldest of these tribes there are traditions that the Creator himself lived, after the creation, with men, and instructed them in their religious, social, and moral obligations. Nowhere do we receive evidence that these religions were developed to a higher degree of perfection by men through their own searching and finding, but, on the contrary, there is decline and deterioration."[10]

So St. Paul was accurate when he described the decline from primitive beliefs to those of his day when he declared, "When they knew God, they glorified him not as God, neither were thankful; but became vain in their imaginations, and their foolish heart was darkened. Professing themselves to be wise, they became fools, and changed the glory of the uncorruptible God into an image made like to corruptible man, and to birds, and to four-footed beasts, and creeping things. Wherefore God also gave them up to uncleanness through the lusts of their own hearts, to dishonour their own bodies between themselves: who changed the truth of God into a lie,

[8] S. M. Zwemer, op. cit., p. 140.
[9] Lecture at UCL; cf. also K. A. Busia on "The Ashanti", *African Worlds*, Ed. D. Forde (Oxford, 1963).
[10] S. M. Zwemer, op. cit., p. 234.

and worshipped and served the creature more than the Creator, who is blessed for ever. Amen." (Rom. 1:21–25).

To the findings of social anthropologists can be added those of pre-historic archaeologists. They are impressed by the fact that as soon as man is able to show some tangible record, he is seen at the outset to be thoroughly religious. In Catal Hüyük, shrines worshipping the mystery of Life abound. At Jericho before the first Neolithic city was built about 7400 B.C., the Natufians were using the site as a shrine. The first city-states of Mesopotamia were centred round temples. The first writing, invented 4000 B.C., was for the purpose of recording the people's gifts and tenths to God or gods.

Does archaeology also indicate that belief in One God came first? Dr. Stephen Langdon, the Assyriologist, of Oxford, reports: "Both in Sumerian and Semitic religions, monotheism preceded polytheism and belief in good and evil spirits. The evidence and reasons for this conclusion, so contrary to accepted and current views, have been set down with care, and with the perception of adverse criticism. It is, I trust, the conclusion of knowledge, and not of audacious preconception". Later he says, "All Semitic tribes appear to have started with a single tribal deity whom they regarded as the Divine Creator of his people." The grounds on which Professor Langdon bases his conclusion are set forth in a brief and acces-sible form in an article entitled, "Monotheism as the Precursor of Poly-theism in Sumerian Religion".[11] He begins by reminding us that the Sumerians were probably the first people to be literate some time about 4000 B.C. From them we obtain the earliest written information concerning the religion of mankind. They were a talented race with a real culture. At Kish, and at Erech, a large number of the oldest writings in the world were found. The facts point unmistakably to monotheism, and a Sky God as the first deity, from whom descended the vast Sumerian pantheon."[12]

It has been argued that if a Supreme Being exists, it would be wrong for him *not* to reveal himself. It would seem that man's religious instinct, like other instincts or drives, is there for a purpose; the appetite for food, the sex-urge for marriage and procreation or sublimation, the implanted universal religious urge for God. If this latter is not fulfilled, there is unsatisfied hunger in the heart. From the moment man records his thoughts in writing in Sumer four millennia B.C., he reveals that religion is at the centre of his social and economic life. Even today's prominent humanist, H. J. Blackham[13], admits this unfulfilled hunger in a chapter headed "The pointlessness of it all" – mankind's craving for religious satisfaction may have led him up winding channels, but that does not dispense with the phenomenon. Indeed the dichotomy between Revealed

[11] *The Evangelical Quarterly*, April, 1937.
[12] S. Langdon, *Semitic Mythology* (Oxford).
[13] H. J. Blackham, *Objections to Humanism* (Constable, 1963), p. 105.

Religion and man's substitutes may be due to a conflict between two inner urges, the desire for religious satisfaction and the unwillingness for it to affect the life too radically – a condition of "paradise lost".

One who claimed to reveal God said, "I am the Bread of Life; he that cometh to me shall never hunger; he that believeth on me shall never thirst" (John 6:35).

Divorced from God, a man's nature is unsatisfied. Even atheists like Haldane and Huxley eventually seek after some sort of religion. As St. Augustine said[14]:

> Thou hast created us for Thyself,
> And our heart knows no rest,
> Until it rests in Thee.

Surprising as it may seem, it is mutual. God also seeks our fellowship with Him. "The Father seeks such to worship Him," declared Jesus (John 4:23). The story of Eden shows that God sought man's love and worship from the beginning, and revealed himself to Adam. He walked in fellowship and communion to the delight and satisfaction of both God and man until that fellowship was broken.

"And they heard the voice of the Lord God walking in the garden in the cool of the day, and Adam and his wife hid themselves from the presence of the Lord God among the trees of the garden," (Gen. 3:8).

[14] *The Confessions of St. Augustine,* A.D. 400, Book I (Fontana, 1957).

CHAPTER VII

SHORT-LIVED AGE OF INNOCENCE

"WHAT EVIDENCE HAS SCIENCE FOR THE FALL?" IS A QUESTION which was asked recently. "Surely we should expect an absence of weapons and scenes of destruction in the age of innocence which must have preceded it!" It is possible that there may be a brief age of purity indicated archaeologically, although little material evidence should be expected.

There appeared to be no need for weapons of war or fortifications in the earliest New Stone Age, or in the first wave of farmers migrating from the initial centre. Mellaart remarks about the absence of war in early Catal Hüyük. This was so with the first Danubians who moved through central Europe, also with Mediterranean coastland migrants who brought their cattle by boat, and with the first Starcovo pre-pottery Neolithic migrants of the Balkans. These are the three main Western streams of migrating farmers.

Likewise, concerning morals, the familiar sexy fertility figurines were absent in those three streams. As for Catal Hüyük, even though the "Fall" would have already taken place, Mellaart remarks "It significantly lacks the element of sexual vulgarity and eroticism that is almost automatically associated with fertility." He suggests the reason might be that the religion of Catal Hüyük was created by women!

Socially too, there were no class distinctions among those Western migrants. All were equals. In other words, it was not a stratified society.

There was a marked difference from the Danubian pioneers when the second Danubian Neolithic peoples traversed Europe over a thousand years later. They built strong stockades around their settlements and provided themselves with effective weapons, and sexy figurines were part of their household goods. The figurines, no doubt, also indicated a less pure religion of superstitious placating of earth gods instead of the Creator and Giver of fruits of earth.

There is another source which has been drawn upon as evidence for the Fall. This is the myths of primitive peoples handed down orally from generation to generation, long before contact with Western civilization. Many social anthropologists think this evidence is significant.

Dr. Zwemer says: "The evidence of anthropology therefore seems to be that of an almost universal tradition of a creation of the world by a High-God in which man occupies a special place as its culmination. Moreover, we find together with this account of man's place in the universe and parallel to it a widely-spread tradition of man's displacement, of a tragedy of disobedience, and the loss of his former state of happiness. Who can resist the conclusion that these many and multiform creation-myths, these constant memories of a lost 'age of innocence' point to a common human tradition and corroborate the scriptural data?"[1]

These myths are called the "World Views" of primitive peoples.

F. M. Savina reports the World View of original inhabitants of China called the Miao: "The Miao hold an essentially monotheistic faith, they have never had a written language, they live in tribes and are an ancient people, having inhabited China before the present Chinese, and been pushed by them towards the mountains in the south. . . . They believe in a Supreme Being, Creator of the world and of men. Death came as a consequence of man's sin: the woman had eaten white strawberries forbidden by the Lord of Heaven. They know of a deluge, followed by a dispersal of peoples."[2]

J. A. MacCulloch reports on the Andamanese who are a preliterate and technologically simple people: "The Andamanese, whose remarkable theology, according to the best authorities, is independent of Christian influence, believe that Puluga, the creator, gave the first man, Tomo, various injunctions, especially concerning certain trees which grew only at one place (Paradise) in the jungle, and which he was not to touch at certain seasons – during the rains, when Puluga himself visits them and partakes. Later, some of Tomo's descendants disobeyed and were severely punished. Others, disregarding Puluga's commands about murder, adultery, theft, etc., and becoming more and more wicked, were drowned in a deluge. Two men and two women survived, and in revenge wished to kill Puluga, who, telling them their friends had been justly punished, disappeared from the earth."[3]

As these primitive peoples with their indigenous stories are farmers, they must have migrated ultimately from the original dispersal centre in the Near East. The farther away they are from that area, the vaguer and more deviated appears to be their oral tradition, which is what might be expected.

The origin of sacrifice comes within the orbit of Social Anthropology. It seems reasonable to assume that the worldwide primitive custom of propitiation by sacrifice had its origin in Adam's Fall. It would appear that the principle of forgiveness through animal sacrifice was revealed to Adam and Eve's family, for year by year the sin offering was offered. After many years had passed, Cain refused to acknowledge his need for atonement, and he offered a bloodless agricultural gift (Gen. 4:3–8).

God did not accept Cain's offering, whose hurt pride erupted into fury. God pointed out that, like Abraham's ram caught in the thicket, a sin-

[1] S. M. Zwemer, op. cit.
[2] F. M. Savina, *Histoire des Miao* (Hongkong).
[3] J. A. MacCulloch, "The Fall", *Encyclopedia of Religion and Ethics*. Vol. 5, p. 707.

offering lay at the door, but Cain refused to accept it. This was one of the earliest of many types and prophecies which were to point to God's provision of a lamb – the Lamb of God – as the final expiation for all men. Cain refused the sin-offering and slew his brother Abel. He followed his own religion of self-salvation and became infuriated with him who trusted in God's provision for sin's atonement.

Prof. Zwemer says that "we have in primitive sacrifice the threefold idea of fellowship, gratitude, and propitiation, with a sense of sin or unworthiness. All of these are not found among all primitives, yet there are clear examples of each form in many far separated cultures, e.g., the Eskimos, the Pygmies, the Algonquins, the Bushmen, and the Veddas."[4]

Prof. Evans-Pritchard describes from his experience of the primitive Nuer tribe in the Upper Nile, the form of their sacrifice.[5] The supplicant presents the ox to be sacrificed to God, then consecrates it by spreading ashes upon the victim's back. This identifies the man with the ox. The supplicant then states the purpose of the sacrifice in the invocation, and pours out in detail his sins and sense of guilt. This can sometimes last an hour. If the sacrifice is to be efficacious everything he says must be true because it is placed upon the back of the sacrificial substitute.

When the supplicant has finished he stands with upraised spear and with a tremendous thrust through the heart slays the ox. In other parts of the world, animals appropriate to the ecology are chosen, e.g., in New Guinea, they sacrifice pigs.

To return to the Bible story, Adam and Eve were given another son, Seth, as a substitute for martyred Abel; and many other sons and daughters were born to them. A long line of descendants who "walked with God" continued in faithfulness, but as the population increased, intermarriage between the godly and the ungodly eclipsed the witness. Lust and violence corrupted mankind until "every imagination of the thoughts of the heart was only evil continually". Only one family "walked with God and found grace in His sight". That was the family of Noah.

We do not know who the "sons of men" were in spite of many suggestions except that they were the ungodly in contrast to those called "the sons of God". (St. Luke calls Adam a son of God.) Perhaps they were Cain's descendants whose genealogical table contains names of those who introduced bigamy and cruel revenge. Cain's wife could either have been one of his sisters whom he married before he became a fugitive, or if other representatives of *Homo sapiens* were in the earth, Cain could have married one of them. If so, it would be these that Cain feared when he said "I shall be a fugitive and wanderer in the earth, and whosoever finds me will slay me".

In any case by the time Adam and Eve were 130 years old (Gen. 5:3),

4 S. M. Zwemer, op. cit.
5 E. E. Evans-Pritchard, *Nuer Religion* (Oxford 1967), pp. 207 ff.

they would have lived long enough for their children and great grand-children to have increased to a population as large as 200,000 and to have travelled some distance. The view that Cain married one of his many sisters, mentioned in Gen. 5:4, is therefore quite feasible. Sometimes, however, it is more effective to reply to an insincere objector's "Where did Cain get his wife from?" by saying that he probably married a Mesolithic Maglemosian!

However, the genealogical table follows Cain's line and shows his descendants not only to be clever inventors, but also promoters of violence and destruction. Recently scientists have been asking the question, "What is wrong with the human race? How is it that man with all his intelligence can act so brutally toward his fellow beings?" Some rejoinder is often made about the behavioural patterns among monkeys!

The Bible claims that it is the result of the Fall, and that this moral mutation has been inherited by all.

Koestler in his symposium "Beyond Reductionism" (September, 1969) says, "Man is an aberrant species, suffering from a biological malfunction, a specific disorder of behaviour which sets him apart from all other species, just as language, science and art set him apart." (Koestler should have added religion). He also described man as the victim of a "subtle engineering mistake" in evolution.

William Thorpe, Professor of Animal Ethology and Director of the Sub-department of Animal Behaviour, Cambridge, is one of the contributors to Koestler's symposium. In an article in *New Scientist* on "Reductionism v. Organicism", he supports Koestler and thinks that materialistic beliefs can make man's plight worse, and lead to some of the major psychiatric disorders current in the world today.

The solution Scripture offers is that Christ can change men's hearts, and give them a conviction of purpose and love, but Christ does so only when invited. Consequently, the human era is only a stage in an unfolding plan.

CHAPTER VIII

THE ORIGIN OF MARRIAGE

ANTHROPOLOGISTS HAVE ALSO EXPRESSED THEIR OPINIONS CONCERNING the origin of marriage customs throughout the world, and here again earlier theories have been revised.

The branch of anthropology within whose orbit this subject comes is known as Social Anthropology. Many taking anthropology as a subsidiary course deal only with this branch. In fact the other branches of anthropology are given in England only at Oxford, Cambridge and University College, London.

The earlier anthropologists like Morgan, McLennan, Tylor and Frazer,[1] took it for granted that early man had no marriage laws or sanctions. They worked on the assumption that early man was promiscuous. This was based upon their own philosophical outlook, and not upon any known facts. Frazer used to write book after book dripping with this plausible stuff. One still sees his book *The Golden Bough* lining the shelves of older and uncritical libraries. Never was so much philosophical nonsense churned out and devoured by the gullible public. Engels was a similar writer.

Others thought that "mother-right" or matriarchy was next in the course of moral evolution.

Professor Radcliffe-Brown of Oxford writing on Kinship and Marriage in 1950, and dismissing such earlier false assumptions said:

"One of the most famous pseudo-historic speculations of the last century was the idea that the earliest form of society was one based on 'matriarchy' or 'mother-right'. One definition of this, given in the *Encyclopaedia Britannica* in 1911 is a term used to express a supposed earliest and lowest form of family life, typical of primitive societies, in which the promiscuous relations of the sexes result in the child's father being unknown. An alternative definition, frequently used, was a social condition in which kinship is reckoned through females only, and in which there would be no recognition of any social relationship of fatherhood. *We have no knowledge of any societies of this kind in the present or in the past*; it is, as Robertson remarked in his History of America in the eighteenth century, a *pure product of imagination*.

---

[1] L. H. Morgan, *Ancient Society* (London, 1877); J. F. McLennan, *Primitive Marriage* London, 1865, Sir J. Frazer, *The Golden Bough* (abridged edition London, 1922). J. Beattie of Oxford writes: "It is reported that even at the end of the nineteenth century the celebrated Sir James Frazer, when asked if he had ever seen one of the primitive people about whose customs he had written so many volumes, tersely replied, "God forbid!" J. Beattie, *Other Cultures* (Cohen and West, 1964), p. 7.

"But early anthropologists also applied the term 'mother-right' to certain existing societies, McLennan to the Nayars of southern India, and Tylor to the Menangkabau Malays."[2]

He continues to say that such lower marriage customs are typical of later and more advanced societies, not earlier primitive societies.

This conforms with what our Lord said in Matthew 19. The slackening of marriage custom came later. "Moses because of the hardness of your hearts suffered you to put away your wives: but from the beginning it was not so." He was referring to Gen. 2:24. "Therefore shall a man leave his father and his mother, and shall cleave unto his wife: and they shall be one flesh."

Again Jacobs and Stern write in their textbook of General Anthropology, "Polygyny, means two or more wives living with one husband in a long term marital union. ... In simple food-gathering economies polygyny was rare but permissible. Since the sexes were of equal status it was not often that a woman wanted another wife in her home. Occasionally, however, she asked her husband to take another wife, or she acceded to his wish for another. However, three or more wives were virtually never found in these societies, if for no other reason than because the lowly economy involved too much labour for the husband in fulfilling his portion of the household's productive work.

"Simple agricultural societies with small surpluses were about as equalitarian as the simple food-gathering societies and therefore had the same sort of freedom of choice for both participants in marital relationships. Hence polygamous unions were extremely rare and they almost never consisted of more than two wives. ...

"It follows that monogamy may well have existed from the very beginnings of culture – that is to say, from Eolithic or earliest Paleolithic (Old Stone Age) times. Promiscuous and brief unions would not have permitted the same degree of survival of dependent youngsters as did monogamous unions.

"The monogamous family and not promiscuity was, then, in all likelihood the earliest form of the family, and it has remained the dominant form in all societies."[3]

Yet means of mass communication still propagate the earlier anthropological concepts, all blissfully regardless! And make these concepts a good excuse for the behaviour which breaks up homes and makes our own modern society less viable to meet life's demands. It would be amusing if not so tragic that those who say that missionaries should not break up the tribal structure of marriage torts, are those who would bring havoc to the structure of Christian society tested over the centuries as being the

[2] A. R. Radcliffe-Brown and Daryll Forde, *African Systems of Kinship and Marriage* (Oxford, 1952), p. 72 ff.; see also A. R. Radcliffe-Brown, *Structure and Function in Primitive Society* (Cohen & West, 1961), p. 76.

[3] Jacobs & Stern, *General Anthropology* (Barnes & Noble, 1959), pp. 153–8.

happiest method for the largest number of people. It has been a major factor in the advance of western society as Desmond Morris also acknowledges.[4] It is interesting to note that even Communist Rŭssia learned this in a costly way. At first the Soviets abandoned Christian marriage laws. The effects were so disastrous that today the Communists are more puritanical than the West, and believe, we think correctly, that promiscuity corrupts society, and jeers at the hypocrisy of Western laxity which pays lip service to Christianity.

When considering the moral question, it should be remembered that a significant difference between human beings and the animals is virginity. Only in the human female does the virginal membrane exist. Although Desmond Morris remarks on this he appears to miss its implication, i.e, that a bride is intended for her husband alone.

The moral question is also related to another exclusive feature, that of a long childhood and adolescence. The purpose of this is self-evident. The immense human brain and character require years of training and learning which consequently need a safe home over the years.

This brain is also capable of moral responsibility, and so what is left to instinct in animals is given to social behaviour in man. The welfare of a nation is bound up with the welfare of its children, therefore it is a society's duty to control those who attempt to corrupt society for their own greedy gain. Morris remarks[5] that this leads to non-pair-bond situations which result in happy homes being broken by temptation.

[4] Desmond Morris, *The Naked Ape*, London, 1967, p. 83.
[5] Ibid., p. 90.

CHAPTER IX

THE TEST BY SUBSEQUENT ARCHAEOLOGY

W E CAN TEST THE VALIDITY OF IDENTIFYING ADAM OF EDEN WITH New Stone Age Man, not only by the culture, but by comparing the succession of events. Archaeological succession subsequent to the Neolithic should accord with that in the Bible.

That our identification is correct is borne out by the fact that it enables the events of the first eleven chapters of Genesis to be taken just as they are in their natural order, and matched with the scientific order of events. This order covers events from the origin of the Universe to the Bronze Age (and indeed, to the Iron Age also). Thus a perfect correlation is achieved by such an alignment.

The details of this alignment of Gen. 1–11 with science, works out as follows:

First, the opening phrase "In the beginning" and the first two verses of Genesis sum up the astro-physical origin of the universe of some nine billion years ago. Second, the days (ages) of creation which follow, align as we have seen, with the geophysics of earth history and with its geology and biology. Third, at the end of the sixth age-day of Gen. 1:26–30, we have Old Stone Age Man. This culture lasted either 500,000 years or two million years. Fourth, in Gen. 2:5 to chapter 4, we have New Stone Age Man with his agricultural revolution in the "Garden of Eden" 10,000 years B.C. This is followed by surprising New Stone Age city developments of Catal Hüyük in Turkey, and Jericho, 8000 to 5000 B.C. Fifth, the Chalcolithic period is referred to in 4:22, when native copper and iron are used 5000 B.C., long before the Bronze Age. Then we have the Flood of Genesis 6–9, between 5000 and 4000 B.C.

The Flood is followed by a new centre of urban civilization. This is the period of the Bronze Age cities of S. Mesopotamian flood valleys, 3500 B.C., with ziggurats like the Tower of Babel. Sumer and Uruk of archaeology, and Shinar of Gen. 10–11, correlate here.

In addition to the chronological alignment between Genesis and science we also have the geographical agreement. The plateau heights of Turkey and Iran before the flood, give place in the story to the alluvial mud-flats of S. Mesopotamia after the flood.

These correlations give an answer to an objection which might be given to account for Adam being represented as Neolithic Man. It is that the writer would take it for granted that men had always known the art of farming. A writer long after the time of Adam, it might be contended, could make this mistake because he would not know of the absence of farming before 10,000 B.C.

This explanation for representing Adam as a Neolithic farmer could be valid were it not that it fitted into the correct order of culture progress given in the story as outlined.

This knowledge could only come from a supernatural source, speaking as it does of events which took place many thousands of years before the writer. Moreover the writer could not have known about Stone Age cities. Such a conception was contrary even to archaeological expectations up to 10 years ago. Neither could the writer have known the locality where farming began, unless it was revealed to him. Even early prehistorians made the mistake of thinking Egypt was the centre.

Moreover, as we have seen, Genesis 1 appears to know of an age before farming, the time of the hunter-gatherer.

Thus Genesis places Neolithic Adam in his correct place of cultural succession.

What was the relationship of the New Stone Age with the Flood? Neolithic culture was able to support very large communities impossible for Old Stone Age hunter-gatherers. The city and population of Catal Hüyük on the Konya Plateau give us good examples of this. They correlate with the text of Genesis which refers to the population increase, "When man began to multiply on the face of the earth, and daughters were born unto them, the sons of God saw the daughters of men that they were fair, and they took them wives of all they chose; and the Lord said, My spirit shall not always strive with man for he also is flesh ..." (Gen. 6:1–3).

This explosion of population and city life brought problems and is represented in Scripture as the prelude to the Flood. The mixed marriages between the godly and the ungodly brought about a dissipation of religion and morals, and an alarming rise of violence. The term "son of God" may refer to those who were sons of God by faith as in John 1:12. The sons of men may be those whom St. Paul would describe as those whose outlook was according to man, who think after the flesh – the natural man who receives not the things of God.

Eventually, "every imagination of the thoughts of the heart was only evil continually," until but one family remained faithful to God – the family of Noah. Before this last bastion of faith crumbled, God decided to send the judgement of the Flood and preserve Noah. The account is an insight into the Creator's policy to preserve biological samples of man and beast to re-populate the earth.

This aligning of Genesis with prehistory has an interesting bearing upon the Flood. It demonstrates that evidence for the Flood does not rest upon the identification of a particular waterlaid stratum of clay. It places the time of the Flood as occurring between the two city-building eras and explains the hiatus between them. The first cities were built in the plateau heights (with the exception of Jericho) which brings a new factor to the question of whether the Flood was local or more widespread. The story of the Flood used to be regarded by many as a tradition arising from an unusually severe flooding of low-lying Mesopotamia. The inhabitants of this alluvial plain experienced many floods, and it was thought that a greater inundation than usual occurred from great waters rushing from the mountain plateaux to the plains.

We see now, however, that the early neolithic farmers had their habitat in the heights of these very plateau lands stretching from Turkey to India. The average altitude was 5,000 ft. with mountains rising to 17,000 ft. It cannot be argued that knowledge was limited to local geography. Trade and travel were widespread. Volcanic glass from Catal Hüyük and other commodities were carried along the trade routes from Turkey to Iran, along the heights to Jarmo and down into the valleys. Stories of local floods would deceive nobody. Moreover, the setting of those figuring in the story is the horticultural gardens of the New Stone Age farmers in the heights. They were those affected. Field farming on a large scale in the low mud flats of South Mesopotamia was of a later era after the Flood. It was this plateau system of which the Bible must be speaking, when it says the mountains and high hills were covered by the Flood. The Bible says also that it was ocean water which invaded the land. Geophysics shows there are a number of ways in which this could happen, but it is not the purpose of this book to give the evidence.

All the descriptions of the second city-building era match the Genesis story after the Flood. Genesis 11 describes how Noah's descendants migrated from the Iranian Plateau into the South Mesopotamian mud flats of Sumer (Shinar), and began to build a ziggurat (Tower of Babel). Finding no stone, they baked bricks and used bitumen for mortar. This was exactly the materials composing the ziggurat at Ur, excavated by Woolley. The Bible represents the Flood as actually causing the hiatus between these two urbanization eras, discovered archaeologically.

This means that O'Connell is not correct in associating the Flood with the hiatus between *Homo neanderthalensis* and *Homo sapiens* much earlier. He is correct in seeing it as a true hiatus and it may even have been caused by an Ice Age flood, but this is not the Flood of Noah, which is clearly placed between the two urbanizations.

Much other valuable information which he gives, however, applies to the Flood of Noah.[1]

The New Stone Age city era on the Turkish-Iranian plateau and at Jericho, commenced 8000 B.C. and ended 5000 B.C. Catal Hüyük ended its history as a city 5000 B.C., when also the Stone Age City of Jericho lay abandoned for 1,000 years.

[1] P. O'Connell, *The Deluge and the Antiquity of Man* (Minnesota, 1959).

Then the Bronze Age city states of the South Mesopotamian plains with the "towers of Babel" or ziggurats commenced 4000 B.C.

It was also before 4000 B.C. that there was a break in the culture of Egypt. A new culture commenced in Egypt after this break, called the Gerzian, having its origin in Mesopotamia. It was Egypt's first advance towards civilization. This break was accompanied by great changes geologically in Egypt where there is a lower water-table due to a new ocean level, and consequently towns were built at a lower level. The Sahara became a desert, having previously enjoyed rich pastures which supported animals. About that time Britain became separated from the Continent (according to geologists; e.g., W. W. Watts, and archaeologists e.g. Gordon Childe).[2] This would also coincide with a gap of nearly 1,000 years between the first New Stone Age migration in Europe (Danubian I, and others), and the second migration (Danubian II).

It was after this hiatus that writing was invented, beginning by records made on small tablets (Fig. 17). Reference has already been made to the similarity of this early writing on tablets, with the short series of tablet-like "Toledoths" in the first eleven chapters of Genesis.

The scattering abroad after the confusion of Babel brought in the Bronze Age Civilization with its many inventions which spread abroad to the world. Its writing, smelting, casting and high-temperature kilns spread from Mesopotamia to established Egyptian civilization 300 years later (Gerzian, 3200 B.C.), and that of India's Indus Valley (3100 B.C.)

This explosion of civilization, literacy and technical attainments is often called the Birth of Civilization.

From this Mesopotamian centre also came Abraham whose ancestors back to Adam had awaited redemption. Abraham believed God's promise that through one of his descendants all the nations of the earth would be blessed. It was fulfilled, of course, in Christ. This promise to Abraham, coming in the twelfth chapter, gives the clue to why the toledoths of the first eleven chapters were preserved. Their very existence and preservation would arise out of the knowledge by Adam's descendants, that this revelation was to be preserved for mankind. Eventually Moses and the prophets of Israel became the guardians to prepare the world for God's salvation.

CORRELATION OF GENESIS WITH ARCHAEOLOGY AND CULTURE SEQUENCES

Before The Flood: Gen. 2:8 to 6:13.

Shanidar-Zarzi complex of caves, and earliest farming experiments 10,000 B.C.

FIRST CITY-BUILDING ERA:

New Stone Age and Chalcolithic Catal Hüyük, Hacilar.

[2] G. Childe, op. cit., p. 31.

Natufian and New Stone Age Jericho.
North Mesopotamian villages of Hassuna and Halaf type.

The Flood: Gen. 6:14 to 9:17.
Post diluvial dispersion, Gen. 9:18 to 10:32.

After the Flood

COMMENCEMENT OF SECOND CITY-BUILDING ERA in South Mesopotamia:

1. Gen. 11:2
   Migration from Ararat along Iranian plateau (Zagros Mountains) south eastwards, then descent from the east on to the flood-plain of Sumer (Shinar) of South Mesopotamia.
   Ubaidian colonization of the marshes (*c.*3900 B.C.); reed huts; irrigation; an important step forward. Some hundreds of years represented by the word "settled" (RSV).

2. Gen. 11:3
   Mud bricks appear first in the Ubaidian phase as there was no mountain-stone available on the mud flats. Even sickles and roof nails were made of baked clay. Warka phase follows.

3. Gen. 11:4
   Proto-literate phase of city states with temples, "Come let us build a city". (*c.*3500 B.C.).
   Ziggurat building commences with heaven-temples at the apex. A ziggurat was a man-made mountain reflecting the mountain origin of the immigrants. Writing commences 3400 B.C.

4. Gen. 11:7–9
   Babel and Erech (Uruk). Confusion and Dispersion. This passage correlates with the stage in the Table of the Nations recorded in Gen. 10:10–14. The relationship of Sumerian and Accadian languages on tablets at this time are an archaeological puzzle.
   Accadian (Accad, Gen. 10:10) migration from the South to North Mesopotamia; then farther northwards to found Assyria and Nineveh, Gen. 10:11.

5. Literate civilization reaches Egypt 200 years later (Gen. 10:13), and reaches the Indus Valley 400 years later (Gen. 10:29, 30).

Correlation of Technology

We find the alignment is correct also as regards the history of the use of stone and the development of metallurgy, i.e.:
New Stone Age followed by "Stone-Copper" (Chalcolithic), and the use

of native copper and haematite in Turkey, and copper smelting at Cayonu. Gen. 4:22.

Bronze Age – 4000 B.C. onwards. Gen. 10–11.

Iron Age – Commenced with the Hittites, 1500 B.C., Deut. 3:11. They held a monopoly of the secret of iron smelting until the eleventh century B.C. Cf. Judges 4:3.

The Philistines acquire it, 1100 B.C. I Sam, 13:19.

Then the Hebrews acquire it, 1000 B.C. II Sam. 12:31.

Fig. 16 : The Strata of a Typical Cave.

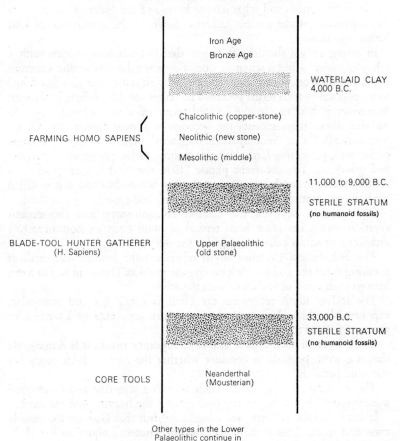

Iron Age

Bronze Age

WATERLAID CLAY 4,000 B.C.

Chalcolithic (copper-stone)

FARMING HOMO SAPIENS

Neolithic (new stone)

Mesolithic (middle)

11,000 to 9,000 B.C.

STERILE STRATUM (no humanoid fossils)

BLADE-TOOL HUNTER GATHERER (H. Sapiens)

Upper Palaeolithic (old stone)

33,000 B.C.

STERILE STRATUM (no humanoid fossils)

CORE TOOLS

Neanderthal (Mousterian)

Other types in the Lower Palaeolithic continue in some caves

CHAPTER X

IN THE BEGINNING

WE HAVE ENDEAVOURED TO ESTABLISH THAT ADAM OF EDEN WAS A New Stone Age man by identifying the culture, and then by aligning the subsequent chronology of Genesis 4–12 with the known archaeological sequence. We must now consider whether we were right in saying that there is a general harmony between the first 25 verses of Genesis and what science knows of the order of events from the beginning of the present universe down to the appearance of Old Stone Age man.

In doing so we should not forget that Genesis was written with a religious object – not a scientific one. The generalized scientific structure is but a framework for religious truth. We must remember also that it had to be phrased in such terms as would be understood by people in all ages. Moreover it had to use the limited terms of a non-scientific age. In meeting these requirements the account is a masterpiece. Dr. D. C. Spanner calls it that "incomparable fragment".[1] It is so brief, yet so comprehensive, presenting Creation with dignity, order, progression, purpose and goodness. The recurrent phrase "God saw that it was good" is a lesson much needed by modern zoologists, whose horizon is over-filled with the conception of a nature "red in tooth and claw".

The contrast between the Genesis creation-story and the ancient creation-myths has often been remarked upon even by commentators unwilling to admit a divine origin for the story.

The Babylonian Creation Myth represents the heaven and earth as resulting from the god Marduk cutting the goddess Tiamat in half to form heaven with one half and earth with the other.

The Indian myth represents the earth as being flat and triangular, supported by three elephants, who are in turn supported by a turtle who swims in a sea of mercury.

In the light of such typical and contemporary myths it is remarkable that it is even possible to consider whether the ancient Bible story has scientific parallels.

The opening sentence of the Bible is both a scientific and theological masterpiece: "In the beginning God created the heavens and the earth."

It states that the universe had a beginning but that God existed outside time and space. This is the conception of Einstein's equation $E = MC^2$. Sir Bernard Lovell of Jodrell Bank, describing in the BBC Reith Lectures the "Big Bang Theory" of the origin of the universe, said, "Time, in the

[1] D. C. Spanner, *Creation and Evolution* (Falcon, 1965, p. 40).

sense of being measured by any clock, did not exist before that moment, and space, in the sense of being measured by any yardstick, was contained entirely within the primeval atom." And again, "On this theory of Gamov all the chemical elements which we deal with today must have been formed within the first thirty minutes of the life of the universe."[2]

Lemaitre also said, "The probable condition of intense radiation in the primeval atom is entirely consistent with the divine command, "Let there be light'."[3]

Sir Bernard Lovell was not necessarily supporting the "big bang" theory of the origin of matter and the universe against the "steady state" theory, which he also outlines. It would be unwise to support any one theory of science against another if there were rival theories, although it should be remembered that a line of investigation is often motivated by what one would call 'philosophical considerations'. In plain language this sometimes means whether a scientist believes in God or not. "Theodore Mommsen's old war cry 'science without presuppositions' carries little weight today," says Professor C. A. Coulson, "for science is personal – deeply personal – in its discovery and in relation to the whole personality of the scientist. We admit now that every scientist comes to his job, not so much with an empty mind as one full of ideas, hunches, feelings, intuitions, hopes, and desires."[4]

From the scientific viewpoint it is useful that experiments on origins should be pressed forward from both the atheistic and the theistic angle, provided that one angle does not become supported by a propaganda machine such as that of Communism. Determination to overweight the atheistic approach both in Russia and in other countries including our own led to inaccurate conclusions. Experimental assessment could not act as the melting pot of theories as it should have done.

The "Big Bang" theory is that the universe had a beginning through the explosion of a dense primeval atom. Fred Hoyle's "Steady State" theory was a rival to this. It suggested that matter always existed and was continually creating itself. It is intriguing to think that were Fred Hoyle right, the old objection – a philosophical one – "Who created God?" would become, "But who created matter?" As Sir Bernard Lovell pointed out, there is a point in science where we go beyond observable facts into philosophy or theology.

The controversy between Hoyle's steady state theory and Gamov and Lemaitre's big bang theory was tested by the Cambridge Radio telescopes in 1964. As a result the big bang theory was pronounced correct, and after a struggle Hoyle conceded the victory. However, after readjusting his

[2] Sir Bernard Lovell, *The Individual and The Universe*, BBC Reith Lectures (OUP, 1958), p. 91.
[3] Ibid., p. 97.
[4] C. A. Coulson, "God, Newton and the Nature of Man": a Review of *Issues in Science and Religion*, by Ian G. Barbour (SCM, 1968).

theory to accommodate the big bang, Hoyle is steadily fighting back. Dr. Peter Stubbs, a science editor of *New Scientist*, reported Hoyle as saying, "I prefer steady state cosmologies, even if it makes life hectic at times." "*His reasons are essentially philosophical*," continues the report. "Why with all eternity to go at, should the primordial atom suddenly decide to blow itself up at one instant? . . . Is it not more satisfactory to envisage a continuing state of affairs in which, even if matter does continually expand outwards" from a centre to "beyond the visible edge of the universe, it is constantly being replaced by the spontaneous creation of new matter?"[5]

The findings of the European Physical Society's Inaugural Conference become relevant here. The consensus of opinion was contrary to Hoyle's theory, and was reported in the April, 1969, issue of *New Scientist* as follows: "The sum total of work on radio source counts and quasars now argues strongly against the steady state theory of Hoyle, Bondi and Gold, and attractive as this may be from a philosophical angle, it now looks as if it must give place to a version of the Big Bang model of the universe."[6]

It will be seen that the knowledge that the universe is an expanding one is shared by all scientists of both theories. The universe is expanding at a rate of one fifth of the speed of light.

It is noticeable that in Genesis light is not attributed to the sun. A mistake is thus avoided which a primitive writer could easily have made, but it is correctly attributed to cosmic light – intense radiation. "This light," says the renowned scientist G. Gamov, "was composed mostly of high energy X-rays and gamma rays. Atoms of ordinary matter were definitely in the minority and were thrown to and fro by powerful streams of light quanta . . . one may almost quote the Biblical statement 'In the beginning there was light'."

It has been pointed out that even Hoyle's steady state theory would not support atheism because even the continuous creation of matter requires an adequate cause. It will have been noticed that Hoyle used the phrase "Spontaneous creation". Much of what is to be said in later chapters, concerning the supposed origin of life by accident (spontaneous generation), applies here also.

Do we have to make up our mind on scientific theories before we can believe the Bible? This would be a most difficult requirement because theories are always changing, yet it is notable that with each change there is left a deposit of knowledge which is a step for the next, and it is remarkable how that this deposit – where there is any certainty – is time and time again in accord with the Bible. However, the revelation of God stands upon its own feet in its religious authority. The Old and New Testaments

[5] New Scientist, April 24, 1969.
[6] See also the BBC publication of the programme, "The Restless Universe", May, 1969.

prove each other in their fulfilment in Jesus Christ, and in the experimental experience of those who act upon them, for God fulfils his promises.

Consequently this book is merely a scientific exercise to meet the propaganda of those who say, "Science disproves the Bible" as if there were a conflict between the two. Educated people have sound reasons for believing the spiritual teaching of the Bible.

The Bible, however, does speak of a beginning to this universe, though there may have been others before it. Indeed the Bible tells us that a different order of beings were created before this universe – spiritual beings. But concerning our present universe, the Bible can be said to make a dogmatic scientific statement that there was a beginning to it. Scientists put its age at 9 billion years. The Bible does not tell us when, only that it was "In the beginning". The word "beginning" in the opening verse, is all the more remarkable because it would be difficult for a primitive to conceive space/time as creations rather than something which always existed, and many primitives did regard matter as eternal.

Einstein's conception that space and time are relative, and that there is a reality outside of space and time is anticipated in the Bible which maintains that God is the eternal "now" or present. He exists outside of space and time. God is there before the beginning:

"I am the Lord who inhabits eternity."
"I am that I am."
"Before Abraham was, I am," said Jesus.[7]

[7] Isaiah 57:15; Exodus 3:15; John 8:58.

CHAPTER XI

THE SIX DAYS

THE OPENING VERSES OF THE BIBLE STATE THAT THE UNIVERSE was created "In the beginning". How long this was before the six days of creation is not given in Holy Scripture. This needs to be emphasized because the jibe is so often repeated that Scripture gives the age of the universe as being 6,000 years, which clearly it does not. After the beginning of the universe – we are not told how long after – the earth is referred to as being in an amorphous state. The Spirit moves upon the face of the waters, there is the fiat of light, and the age-days of earth's development follow.

As we examine each age-day in succession, it will be seen that the order of development is similar to the scientific one. If we take the days as being age-days of many millions of years' duration we shall see that this time-scale is also similar.

To anticipate an objection, this does not mean that the Bible age-days are to be identified with the start and finish of any particular geological epoch or era. These geological divisions are artificial conveniences of terminology to do with rock systems. The biological divisions are again different and although called ages they vary in length according to what form of life was dominant e.g., Age of Fishes, Age of Amphibians.

We can tell where the Bible age-days start and finish by the kind of event or life described. The sixth day began, for example, with the appearance of the first reptiles in the Permian period about 250 million years ago. The fifth day probably began with the Cambrian 570 million years ago when there was a "sudden appearance of representatives of nearly all the classes of animals without backbone (invertebrate phyla)", in the words of Manchester Museum geological column.

Genesis tells us that this earth history of development was not the result of blind chance, but was guided by God's instructions within the natural orders so that they are to "bring forth" or develop God's requirements.

Many of our modern scientific terms use archaic words like "atom" and reclothe them with a modern meaning. Originally the word meant the smallest indivisible unit of matter which Leucippus, 400 B.C. conceived as being solid like a marble, a very primitive conception. Similarly the words of Hebrew cosmogony are used and reclothed with meaning to describe God's creation. So forget those fond drawings in some school textbooks of the Hebrew universe.

We now examine the age-days of earth's development:

Day One. God divides the light from darkness. The first day begins in darkness, even though God had created light two verses earlier. Judging from other planets this day's darkness on the earth's surface would be caused by dense gases, steam and dust lasting millions of years. Under the heading "Early stages of the Earth", the British Museum handbook says, "For long ages the earth was surrounded by a thick, steamy atmosphere."[1] Eventually light would penetrate. "The evening and morning were the first day." That the day started with the long ages of darkness, confirms the age-day interpretation.

Day Two. In the second day the vapour from earth's interior would condense in seas and clouds, the atmosphere ("firmament", in limited Hebrew vocabulary) dividing them. The British Museum handbook says, "As soon as the surface became cool enough, the water-vapour condensed as rain, producing rivers and seas."[2] The earth was just the right size and gravity for retaining its water and atmosphere. On smaller planets they were lost into space.

Dr. R. E. D. Clark comments, "The story of the early stages of the earth's formation is told in the first chapter of Genesis and in the thirty-eighth chapter of Job. The agreement with modern views is remarkable. . . . We are told that the ocean 'burst forth from the womb' – an apt metaphor. When the earth's surface was hot, some or all of the ocean must have been in the form of steam which would have shielded the earth from the sun's rays, so that 'there was darkness over the face of the deep'. Under the great pressure caused by hot vapours above, so-called 'critical' conditions would have been reached so that at first there would be no distinction between vapour and liquid. . . . As condensation proceeded, diffuse light must have percolated through the clouds, and in time day and night were distinguishable, though the sun and moon would not at first be visible. Later there must have been a time when the mists rose, forming clear sky between the liquid water below and the cloud cover above – the clear sky being the 'firmament' ('God called the firmament heaven', i.e. sky)."[3] This was the only era which God did not pronounce "good". Was it the time Satan fell, as prince of the atmosphere (Eph. 2:2), with authority (Luke 4:6, 7), in this mineralogical era? (Ezekiel 28:13, 14). Interference with creation may date from then (Romans 8:19–22).

Day Three. The third day sees the formation of the continental masses as one great continent floating upon a viscous sima, as it is called today. The conception here would seem to support the modern Continental Drift theory, or its equivalent Plate Tectonic Theory.[4] The old theory

---

[1] Oakley and Muir-Wood *Succession of Life through Geological Time* (Br. Museum, 1962), p. 4.
[2] Ibid.
[3] R. E. D. Clark, *The Christian Stake in Science* (Paternoster Press, 1967), p. 133.
[4] The Continental Drift theory is being replaced by a theory called the *Plate Tectonic* theory. This appears to give the same results as continental drift but accomplishes it by a different process – namely by the transport of material from ocean troughs to continental margins.

held for so long postulated that land arose through crust shrinkage like a dried orange skin. This view became untenable because if this were the case we should expect to see an equal distribution throughout the world of ridges of land and troughs of sea. It did not explain why there was a sea hemisphere and a continental mass hemisphere. In modern terms the mountains are seen to have roots – the higher the mountainous mass the deeper the roots into the sima. Perhaps this is an equivalent to the biblical phrase "pillars of the earth". As those who have learnt physical geography know, the effect is rather that of a submerged iceberg. This balance of the height of mountains with the depth of continental roots is poetically described by God to Isaiah in 40:12:

> Who weighed the mountains in scales,
> And the hills in a balance?
> Who has directed the Spirit of the Lord,
> Whom did he consult for his enlightenment?
> ... The Lord is the everlasting God,
> Creator of the ends of the earth.

Later that third day the land brings forth Plant Life at God's word. The Hebrew for plant life indicates its early stages. Plant life had to precede land animals for billions of years, in order to extract from the atmosphere poisonous carbon dioxide and put oxygen into the atmosphere for animals to breathe.

"Most of the free oxygen now present has been produced by the activities of green plant life" (British Museum Handbook).[5]

Although less is known about the origin of plant life most diagrams show plant life (flora) as coming before marine animals. In any case flora cells with chloroplasts are acknowledged to be the first to appear. An early land plant has been reported from the Middle Cambrian, and there is an investigation into the possibility of plant life having begun in land pools rather than in the oceans.

Other planets have no oxygen, or practically none. Professor Rendle Short wrote: "We have already seen reason to believe that animal life was not possible until there was vegetation to supply oxygen to the atmosphere. The word *deshe*, translated 'grass', means something green, and no doubt covers all kinds of green plants of a lowly type. It is noteworthy that the Coal Measure ferns were seed-bearing. Seed-bearing plants are therefore very old."

Day Four. On the fourth day the atmosphere, which so far has only admitted light, clears sufficiently for the sun, moon and stars to be seen. Hence their introduction as "lights" (v. 14). That they were already in existence is indicated by the Hebrew perfect tense two verses later, which states their completedness rather than the time of the action. This is a

[5] Op. cit., p. 5.

peculiarity of Hebrew tenses. Before this, the earth would look like Jupiter wrapped in bands of dense cloud. See Job's description of the earth wrapped in swaddling bands (Job 38:9). Professor Rendle Short says: "the clouds now cleared sufficiently to allow the Sun, Moon and Stars to be seen from the Earth's surface. All through the Creation-narrative the observer is regarded as being on the Earth's surface."

Day Five. On the fifth day, the account correctly says that marine life was the first animal life. "Let the waters bring forth swarms of life, with which the waters swarm." Notice how the emphasis is on the swarming life (see RSV). Geologists like myself have chipped out masses of trilobites, molluscs, corals, etc., fossilized in these Cambrian seas. "After their kind." All the phyla except the vertebrates had appeared by then.

Eventually the great sea-monsters appear. The Plesiosauruses 80 ft long, and like creatures, always excite the imagination. The RSV translation is better here than the AV. The word "whales" of the AV translation is not in the Hebrew.

"Let winged things multiply on the earth." The Hebrew does not say "birds" as in the AV translation, or even "winged birds" as the RSV translation of 1952.

The Hebrew says "winged things" as of insects. This shows how the inspired Hebrew of so long ago is more accurate than a modern translation. Science shows that insects were the first flying creatures and appeared at this point. "Winged insects appeared in great variety in Upper Carboniferous times, and included primitive cockroaches and types resembling dragonflies as well as forms now totally extinct, such as the 'six-winged' Palaeodictyoptera. A dragonfly, Meganeura, preserved as an impression in the coal shales of Commentry, France, had a wing span of 29 in. and is one of the largest insects known."[6]

It is remarkable how insects appeared at the same time as pollen-bearing flowers (Angio-sperms). One could not exist without the other for longer even than one summer. The British Museum pamphlet on the geological record remarks upon this. "The spread of insects was probably associated with the appearance of flowers, for many flowers and insects are mutually dependent, the insects pollinating the flowers and being repaid by nectar.'[7] It seems impossible that coincidence would account for this symbiosis which of necessity must be viable for both species within a brief time limit, especially as they belong to two entirely different kingdoms of flora and fauna.

Day Six. On the sixth and last day appear (in correct order of life) the land animals. The Reptiles (in the Cenozoic) and the first Mammals (in the

[6] Ibid., p. 24.
[7] R. L. Sherlock, *A Guide to the Geological Column* (Dept. of Scientific & Industrial Research, London), p. 5.

Eozoic). Man appears later on in this sixth age-day. In view of man's importance it is significant that there is not allotted him a separate day of creation. The representation of man's appearance late in the day is correct, for man's Pleistocene era occupies only a relatively brief time-span, even though it might represent two million years.

We have already shown that Old Stone Age man appears first, as depicted, within the context of an age-day, and that New Stone Age Adam is a child of only a few thousand years.

Professor Rendle Short says: "The final act of creation was to bring man into the world. 'And God said, Let us make man in our image, after our likeness'. Fossil man appeared on the Earth much later than the other mammals, certainly during the Ice Age, perhaps during Pliocene times.

"These considerations bring to light a perfectly amazing accordance between the Creation-narrative and the discoveries of modern science. When we remember the wild guesses as to the ultimate nature and origin of the earth that were current amongst other ancient people, the accuracy of Genesis stands out in solitary grandeur. Geology is a young science; the classification of strata is not much older than a hundred years; we may be sure the author of the Creation-narrative derived none of his information from fossil-hunting. Neither guesswork nor intuition taught the writer to arrange events in the correct order. This narrative bears the marks of a divine inspiration."[8]

Man was created then, within the context of age-days. This applies to both Old and New Stone Ages, which was why our Lord could link the two in his remark in Matthew 19:4-6. But it was at the very end of the sixth age-day that Adam of Eden, the New Stone Age farmer, came upon the scene. It is with regard to this New Stone Age ancestor that the second tablet or toledoth takes up the story in Gen. 2:4. It does so with the brief recapitulation of relevant points typical of a Sumerian toledoth tablet which links it as a sequel to the preceding tablet.[9] Although the sixth

---

[8] Rendle Short, *Modern Discovery and The Bible* (IVF, 1943), p. 66.

[9] The **Eleven Toledoths**, or Sagas, of Genesis are: Gen. 2:4, of the Creation (Summarizes preceding passage Gen. 1:1 to 2:3); Gen. 5:1, of Man and Adam (Summarizes creation of Man and of the Adam. See RSV. Then selects one of Adam's sons); Gen. 6:9, of Noah (Summarizes Gen. 5:29 to 6:8. Note that no genealogical table follows); Gen. 10:1 of the Three Sons of Noah (Summarizes the preceding Gen. 6:9 to 9:29 and the Table of Nations which follows); Gen. 11:10, of Shem (the Semitic peoples). The generations of the five sons of Shem precede this toledoth, which then selects the one of Shem's sons from whom Abraham is descended; Gen. 11:27, of Terah (father of Abraham). Summarizes preceding verse, then continues; Gen. 25:12, of Ishmael (Abraham's Son). Summarizes Gen. 16, and then gives table of descendants; Gen. 25:19, 20 of Isaac (Abraham's Son). Refers to Isaac's life in the preceding chapters. No genealogical table follows but the lives of Esau and Jacob follow; Gen. 36:1, 2, of Esau (who is Edom). Isaac's son. Refers to Gen. 26:34, 35 and then gives table of descendants; Gen. 36:9, of Esau's Sons. Refers to preceding eight verses and then gives table of descendants; Gen. 37:2, of Jacob. The Saga of Jacob is contained in nine preceding chapters

age-day in the preceding tablet (Genesis 1) was a comprehensive statement of mankind's creation, the scene had been occupied mainly by Old Stone Age man for the greater length of time. So it is left to the second tablet to speak specifically of the New Stone Age; and for good reason, for the rest[10] of the Bible was to be about the salvation of his descendants.

We have now completed our chronological alignment of Genesis with science and prehistory and demonstrated that the identification of Adam with the Neolithic Revolution fits in well with this chronology.

(Gen. 27–35); the Saga of Joseph follows (Gen. 37–50), with that of the twelve tribes (Gen. 46, 49).

Thus, the characteristic of a toledoth is **to sum up the preceding instalment** before introducing the sequel. This does not commit us necessarily to Wiseman's theory that it appeared at the base of the tablet. It could just as well appear at the head, or be the caption on the clay envelope containing the tablet. Its purpose, however, seems clear - to provide the link between instalments of tablet sagas.

[10] As tablets 2, 4 5 and 6 select towards Abraham, it is possible that Abraham co-ordinated and recorded what had been passed on from his ancestors. From Abraham onwards the narrative becomes fuller and more verbose.

CHAPTER XII

ADAM'S CELLS

WE COME NOW TO A MORE PROFOUND PROBLEM. SCIENCE IS turning its attention to the biological history of the basic consti-tuents of life; the bio-chemistry and molecular history which are shared by all living things. Our red blood corpuscles have a history older than mammals; proteins present in the human body come from the dawn of life. The genetic system of genes, chromosomes and DNA, are shared by all living creatures of the past and present, whether they are mice, men, salmon or sunflowers.

As Dr. Graham Chedd said in January, 1969, during the previous twelve years biologists had come to a new understanding of life's underlying unity: "The fundamental molecules and mechanisms in a cabbage are the same as those of a man."[1]

It might be felt that the evidence outlined in the preceding chapters, gives weight to the possibility that the present race of *Homo sapiens* has no ancestral connexions with any earlier fossil man, that Adam was a new species created from scratch. But what of Adam's cells? The cells which make up the human body share common features with preceding life: Does this imply a genetic connexion? Even if we consider Adam to be a new species, we have to consider the origin of his components.

From the theological viewpoint we have some biological principles of Scripture to guide us.

First, we note that this underlying unity of life is implied in the Genesis story of Creation. Plant life is depicted as reproducing after its kind by the seed which is in itself; likewise, man is to be fruitful and his offspring is referred to as his seed. Modern genetics have confirmed this remarkable insight of Scripture, that the genetic mechanism of reproduction is similar for plants, animals and man.

This underlying unity of life is implied also in the second toledoth (Genesis 2). Here it is declared that the Lord God formed man of the dust of the ground (v.7), and the animals are given a similar origin in verse 19, "Out of the ground the Lord God formed" the animals and brought them to Adam to see what name he would give them. As is common to Hebrew style this does not necessarily mean the animals were created in Eden at that point in the story, but that having been formed according to the first toledoth earlier in the sixth age-day, they were made available to Adam for domestication.

It is a notable fact that the animals which neolithic man domesticated, the dog, cat, sheep, goats, cattle, etc., were native to that part of Western

[1] Graham Chedd, *What is Life?* (BBC Publications 1968), p. 1.

Asia. The story is a supplement to the process described in Gen. 1:24, "God said, let the earth bring forth the living creature after its kind."

The common origin of man and animals from elements contained in the earth is reflected in the remarkable fact that despite the complexity of life's mechanism, out of the 90-odd different sorts of atoms available in nature to build with, life uses only six to any large extent. These are carbon, hydrogen, oxygen, nitrogen, sulphur and phosphorus. They are the main atoms occurring repeatedly in molecular structure throughout the history of life on earth. Many other atoms, such as metals, appear only in small quantities.

The creative significance of words such as "God said", in the light of genetic coding, will be considered more fully later. It is coupled with such expressions as "Let the waters bring forth life", "Let the earth bring forth life". The words "bring forth" suggest that a natural process is involved.

The difficulty which many geneticists see, however, was expressed by Prof. Ronald Good in a BBC science series, "Natural Selection Re-examined". He said, "No amount of selection can initiate novelty", i.e., produce anything new.[2]

In other words, at present science has no mechanism to produce a more complicated creature such as man, from a lower order. The present theory of natural selection can only explain variety in an existing type, but not the initiation of a new higher type. The arguments concerning industrial melanism in moths, fruit flies, mutations and the like, do not affect the issue.

This principle of using a pre-existent cell is seen in the story of the origin of Eve if we take it at its face value. Although Eve is a new being, she was not created out of nothing, but from the cells of Adam's body. Did the same apply to the females referred to in Chapter I, "God created man in his own image . . . male and female created he them." We would have no hint in that passage that they might have been created from a pre-existent cell, but for the story of Eve.

Further, did Eve, through Adam, have molecular affinity with all animal life?

Eve is represented as being made from Adam's side as the result of a surgical operation. We cannot be sure of the meaning of the Hebrew word translated 'rib', but that does not matter. Whatever part of Adam's body was used, it would involve the use of somatic or body-cells. This operation has affinities with a startling experiment carried out in 1967. It showed that a genius like Einstein could be genetically preserved and reproduced for mankind. Although the experiment was carried out on animals, it would equally apply to human beings.

In the experiment, a body-cell and not a sex-cell,[3] was used for reproduction of a toad. The cell was taken from a toad's gut, although it

[2] R. Good "Natural Selection Re-examined", *The Listener*, May 7, 1959.
[3] This phrase is coined for the general reader. By it is meant cells (ova and sperms) produced by sex organs.

could have been taken from any part of the animal. The mechanism for meiotic division was supplied from cytoplasm of a rabbit. Another toad was reproduced as a result, which, though a generation younger, was the identical genetic constitution of the former.

If the story of Eve is to be taken literally, this seems to be similar to what God did to supply a genetically compatible mate. From Adam's body-cells God produced a woman. The "Y" chromosome which changes the being to a male, would be omitted, and then the being produced would automatically be a female e.g., similar to a Klinefelter's syndrome with "XX" but omitting "Y", with compatible genes to perpetuate the new species on marriage.[4] So Adam could truly say that Eve was "Flesh of my flesh" or body-cells of my body-cells, and when married they became one flesh. This would make Eve an identical twin to Adam, except that it has been shown by R. Williams and others that there can be minor variations in identical twins. These variations come from the cytoplasm which surrounds the cell's nucleus. Mutations would produce further variations later.

In order to follow the argument about what connexion the cells of Adam and Eve may have with creation as a whole, we need to have a general picture of the mechanisms of the cell. The understanding of the cell will also be necessary when we discuss whether life could arise by accident. Even those familiar with the mechanism of the two types of cell would profit from reading the following description, as many of the analogies will be referred to in our argument.

There are two main types of cell:

1. Those which pass on heredity, which for clarity I will call sex-cells.
2. Those which make up the human body.

The animal body is made up of cells. Some animals consist of one cell only, such as the amoeba and other protozoa. Every human begins as a single cell after fertilization. This cell becomes an embryo in the womb by dividing and multiplying rapidly into thousands of cells. These cells make up the body and become limbs, organs, nerves, brain or blood cells, according to their position in the body.

When the cells have become a complete body they still carry out the vital metabolic functions to keep that body alive and working. The cell is therefore the basic unit of the animal body, the factory of life, a factory more complex than any built by man, and the simplest way to understand the functions of the cell is to describe them through the analogy of a fully automated factory.

In both types of cell the central management is housed in the director's office, called the nucleus. This is in the centre of the cell and divided from the surrounding cytoplasm by a membrane as the office partition.

[4] Further experiments were made by Dr. J. B. Gurdon of Oxford. "Transplanted Nuclei and Cell Differentiation," *Scientific American*, Dec. 1968.

Both types of cell – the sex-cell for heredity and the body – or somatic cell – have all the same information housed in the central office. This information is really a long list of instructions for producing another person, animal or plant. It is exceedingly detailed and is recorded on DNA strands composed of volumes called Chromosomes and chapters called Genes. These again are divided into sentences.

Although the instructions have been divided into what has been described as books and chapters, we must not think of pages, but rather of a computer tape. A computer tape consists of a long ribbon of punch-hole code instructions, but the DNA strand registers the information in nucleic acids of which there are four. We will call them by their initial letters, A, C, G and T.

This record is in code which Gamov described as similar to a Morse Code. Its four symbols, the nucleic acids, require interpretation into three lettered words.

If the DNA[5] code were recorded in books, it would fill hundreds of our normal-sized volumes, but in the central office of a human cell, it is recorded in 23 large volumes. There is a second copy, because each one was derived from the two parents, thus making a total of 46

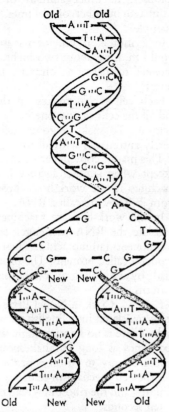

Fig. 17: The DNA strand which contains the genetic instructions. During the division of a cell to form two daughter cells, the double helix of DNA also divides and forms two daughter helices. This it does by unwinding itself; each strand then acts as the template for the formation of a new strand which is its copy (RNA).

[5] DNA stands for deoxyribonucleic acid. These are the nucleic acids which are the medium upon which is recorded the four-letter code. They are Adenine, Cytosine, Guanine and Thymine and they are usually abbreviated to their initial letters: A.C.G. and T. On these are recorded the genetic information passed from parent to offspring. These are linked together like a spiral staircase by sugar and phosphate bonds to make a chain.

RNA stands for ribonucleic acid. In this copy of the DNA message one of the four bases recording the master-copy is changed – uracil replaces thymine, but the same message is recorded.

volumes. In other animals or plants the message is contained in a different number of volumes, 18 for a cabbage, 66 for a horse, for example.

In a mouse, if one of its 40 chromosomes were stretched out, it would measure about two inches. If the width of the DNA strand was widened to that of a computer tape, the relative length would be 400 miles!

Each cell which makes up the body can be likened to a factory, and all the cells of any one body could be likened to a firm with many factories. To make a good analogy, all the factories should be completely automatic, with all their processes controlled by the master tape.

This master copy never leaves the safe custody of the managerial office except when another factory is established. The instructions reach the machines in the workshops through a series of messenger tapes copied from it. They are called RNA.

In the workshop are machines called ribosomes which read off and translate the RNA messenger tape and produce 20 different kinds of components (amino acids). These in turn are assembled into 80 different products called proteins. The proteins are the basics of life and each one is made by assembling over a thousand component amino acids into various patterns.

F. H. C. Crick, a Nobel Prizewinner, says that if this language of life were translated into English, it would occupy 1,000 books of 500 pages each. There is no known single writing of man as long as this. It is about 300 times as long as Shakespeare's plays. The *Encyclopaedia Britannica* would occupy 56 volumes of this size, which is far less than a thousand! Yet the cell mechanism makes a complete copy of its 1,000 books in 20 minutes, and the ribosomes read off the code, computerwise, for a protein in ten seconds!

There are 15,000 ribosome machines in any one cell producing the components. Each one is very complex and all are co-ordinated into a production line, so it is an exceedingly large factory.[6] The machines are attended by robot workmen called enzymes, who recognize the place in the growing assembly line to plug in their amino acid to make the correct protein.

If the robots were to plug their components into the wrong sequence among a thousand or so others, it might prove disastrous.

These robot mechanics belong to one of 200 trades.[7] Each one is a specialist with machine tools for his own exclusive operation, and a lock and key to start and stop his own machinery. So there must be 200 trade unions, but the enzyme robots are hard workers, for each one turns out half-a-million molecules per minute!

[6] *Science Journal*, 1971, p. 410: "Nature's protein factory, the ribosome, is a hugely complicated structure."

[7] About 1,000 enzymes are known, but only 200 crop up repeatedly in every living species.

For some operations the worker has an assistant worker called a co-enzyme, and in addition there is a robot worker to control each step in the mass-production line.

All these robots obey explicitly the instruction tapes brought to them by the messengers. They bring the tape from their foreman, the gene who controls the correct sequence, and has copied the instructions from the master-tape (DNA).

There are several kinds of messengers who go between Headquarters and workshop and copy, carry and translate the message for the particular piece of workshop machinery.

There is also a departmental manager who co-ordinates his shop to concentrate on producing a particular line of goods, whether it is a hair on the head, or an eye, or leg sinew. He sends into the shop inducers and repressors to switch on or off by regulator gene the required machinery, otherwise one could get a leg growing out of one's head, or all the body could be an eye, to use St. Paul's phrase. This is because every cell has the potential to produce a complete man, yet the cell may be required to produce only a hair at a particular part of the body.

There seems to be a three-dimensional graph by which a cell is numbered to do its job. The relevant machinery is switched on according to its longitude, latitude, or depth, relative to the body's orientation. As Jesus said, even the very hairs of your head are all numbered.

According to Professor Monod, 99 per cent of the genes and the machinery they control are switched off at any one time. Professor Jacques Monod, of the Pasteur Institute of Paris, is eminent for his research in this field, and in his Science Lecture on BBC Television he concluded, "God the Father is a wonderful mechanical engineer."[8]

It may be because every cell has the potential for producing any part of the body if the control genes are switched on, that Jesus was able to make eyes for the blind man from the saliva cells of his mouth when he pressed them with clay into the man's eye sockets. The saliva cells are favourite cells to use under the microscope because they are so large. It gives one a rather uncanny feeling to look at one's own saliva cells. They are scraped from the inside of one's own mouth and placed under a microscope. When magnified one can number and identify all the two sets of 23 chromosomes. One student declared humorously that it was the first time he was convinced he was a man when he recognized his own "Y" chromosome!

The reason why it is important to produce the correct protein is that the protein determines what component in the body the cell is going to be. The strange thing is that in producing that protein the cell forms itself into that component to join up with neighbouring cells. A good analogy is Mulberry Harbour of "D"-Day in the Second World War. Mulberry Harbour was so called because the concrete barges which made their way

[8] François Jacob and Jacques Monod.

across the channel, grew into a harbour on reaching their destination. They were so shaped that they fitted into and linked up with the neighbouring barges to form a quay for our invading troops. Thus the four thousand million cells of our body link together as organs to make a complete human body: the body then becomes a machine working as a unit. It is a machine in which each organ itself surpasses in excellence similar machines made by man. The eye works on a television camera principle, but with a much finer screen; the muscles retract and extend on the electric solenoid principle; and the brain would be equalled in complexity only if there were enough computers stacked side by side to fill all the land areas of the world. Unlike man-made wonders the body is also a machine equipped with emotion, feeling and psyche.

The factory-cells of the body have time-switches preset to come on at given times between birth and death. Within 24 hours after birth for example, the body's network of police stations (the Lymphocytes) are alerted against industrial spies attempting sabotage. By industrial saboteurs we mean germs, foreign protein and tissue. This is what causes the rejection of heart transplants. In the baby it gives immunity against harmful bacteria, etc. Why is the body's police network timed to operate within a few hours of birth, and not before? Undoubtedly it is because if the system were switched on before birth, the baby would reject its mother's nourishment.

The baby's Scotland Yard which alerts the Police Stations is called the thymus. It is situated in the chest. Once the thymus has switched on the body's police stations, its job is completed for life. From then onwards the police go around the body arresting and ejecting every suspect who is not wearing the body's own particular identity badge. Indeed, the police stations have their own forensic laboratories in which they make a chemical analysis of any new foreign agents. The laboratory would be labelled "Immunology Dept.".

Later, at puberty (12 to 14 years), the time-switch comes on for the sex hormones to commence their function, then between the ages of 40 and 50 years the time-switch for the change of life operates. As the three-score-years-and-ten approach, an ageing device operates for the running down of the machinery. Specialists agree that ageing is not the result of machinery wearing out, for cells constantly renew themselves. There seems no reason why the body should not live for ever, apart from some preset clock which says "start the count down".

There is an important department we have not considered. It is the Ministry of Fuel and Power. This has its machinery, called the mitochondrion, in each factory-cell. It has been described as being as complex as another fully-automated factory in itself. There are several in each cell and they manufacture and supply fuel or energy for every machine, robot, messenger and managerial tape, in the factory. It has grades of fuel – not commercial grades of course – but high octane and low octane called ATP and ADP[9] respectively. The supply of these grades is controlled by check switches, otherwise the cell would burn itself out if it had high grade all the time. This significant feature of the cell-mechanism will be more fully considered when we discuss the origin of life.

There are two methods of reproduction. The first is that of the body-cell. Each cell in the body divides in order either to make the body grow, or if it has finished growing, to replace old cells.

To follow our analogy, not only has each factory-like cell the ability to produce one main line of goods, it can also produce another factory automatically to take its place alongside and commence production. This it does periodically.

First the master-tape of directive instructions has to be recopied on the flexowriters by the copytypists so that each new factory has its full complement of 46 volumes in the case of man. This means there are now 92 – two lots of 46. When the copies are complete, the office partition collapses. Ropes are attached to one lot of 46 tape reproducers and their tapes, and likewise ropes to the other 46. The one bundle of 46 ropes coming from the reproducers in the centre are attached to a mechanical horse, called centriole near one pole of the central office. At the other pole there is another mechanical horse with its 46 ropes attached to the second group of 46 volumes. At a word from the managing director the mechanical horses pull their clusters of 46 volumes away from the centre in opposite directions by winding up their ropes. Meanwhile each of the 15,000 production and assembly machines and the power plants has reproduced itself and they all regroup around the two new centres of 46 chromosomes. The factory walls enlarge, and the central office re-erects its partition around the tape reproducers. The one factory has now become two factories.

What has been described above is called mitotic division. Our bodies start as one cell. This factory increases by division and sub-division in this manner until our bodies are composed of as many factories or cells as there are people on this earth.

The analogy now needs developing to explain the mechanics of the sex-cells' reproduction.

In commercial life a firm may have many factories. Let it be supposed that two large firms have decided to amalgamate. We shall now have what is equivalent to division, in the sex cell. Each male or female cell divides into four instead of two, like the body cell, in order to produce a daughter cell with only half the number of chromosomes. This division is called meiosis. We suppose, then, that two large firms have decided to merge.

If we liken the 46 volumes of instructions to 46 managers constituting the Company's Board of Directors; by the merging of the two firms, half

[9] ATP and ADP stand for adenosine triphosphate and adenosine diphosphate. The ATP-ADP system is an energy store into which the cell can deposit the energy it gets from oxidizing glucose by a complex process.

will become redundant. A sorting out must take place and each successful manager displaces the retiring manager. Before the merger, the firms make their own selection, however, so the mechanical horses have only 23 reproducers to drag into the new office. On merging with the 23 of the other firm, the number 46 is restored.

But what of the two heads of the firms? Supposing one is a female director of a women's clothiers, named Miss Dorothy Hoskins, and the other is a men's clothiers headed by a Mr. Montague Bilton, then the takeover will be decided by lottery. Marked cards are placed in a hat so to speak marked with "X"s and "Y"s. These represent the sex-determining chromosomes. At the ballot four cards are available, of which two have to be withdrawn. If both are "X"s, then the woman director takes over (i.e. the body becomes female), but if the two cards have one "Y", the male director takes over, even if there were also three "X"s among the cards. This is because "Y" is dominant over any number of "X"s if present. The issue is not so loaded in one direction as it seems, however. Actually there is almost a 50/50 chance of male or female directorship because there are three times as many "X"s in the hat as "Y"s.

The 46 successful managers now combine in their mastertapes the selective characteristics from both parent firms, but a certain percentage of the records of the old firm are always kept, so that an old feature could always be reintroduced in succeeding generations. It is this constant re-shuffling of DNA tapes which makes national and racial characteristics possible.

CHAPTER XIII

THE IMPASSE FOR "ORIGIN OF LIFE" BIOLOGISTS

FOR THOSE WHO ATTEMPT TO EXPLAIN THE ORIGIN OF LIFE ON purely materialistic grounds, a new problem has appeared. The DNA instruction tapes of the cell are made of materials which are different from the products. So it is difficult to see how one could evolve from the other without some creative agency. These difficulties are frankly admitted, and the answers attempted have so far been unconvincing. Likewise, the willingness of some to accept inadequate answers uncritically must be suspect.

Materialists were really unaware of this problem until the 1960's. They thought they could explain the accidental origin of the products, namely proteins and enzymes, and ignore the existence of a factory to produce them – a factory whose existence also had to be explained.

As Orgel has expressed it,[1] we are faced again with the classic chicken and egg problem. This problem, however, is expressed in such terms as, "Which came first: proteins or nucleic acid?" Consequently the fallacies of the argument are often obscured to the non-specialist.

Before the present problem appeared on the horizon, even the attempts to explain the accidental formation of the products had been unconvincing. Let us liken the product of life to an airliner. This is a reasonable illustration because the most complex mechanism evolved by man is comparatively simple compared with products of the cell. As Bernal says concerning life's origins, "Protoplasm is no more seen as a homogeneous lump of slime but an industry of highly complex machinery."[2] And again, "Every cell and still more, every organism, is as complex as the most complex machine built by man."[3]

When the Melanesian New Stone Age natives were discovered this century the natives debated the origin of the white man's goods and aeroplanes. Some tribes were unwilling to believe that the white man had manufactured them in his own factories. They had never seen a factory, so why believe in them? They were also unwilling to think that the white man had outwitted the spirits of their ancestors.

Eventually they hit upon an amusing explanation called "Cargo", as we shall see, but in order to illustrate our points we shall imagine a conversation which might have ensued between a native and a white man. If the analogy seems ludicrous it should be remembered that it reflects the

---

[1] Orgel, *Journal of Molecular Biology*, Vol. 38, January, 1969, pp. 367–81.
[2] J. D. Bernal, *Origin of Life* (Weidenfeld & Nicolson, 1967), pp. 209.
[3] J. D. Bernal, "Definitions of Life" *New Scientist*, 1967.

arguments of some "Origin of Life" biologists, but stripped of their technical language, which can often hide fallacies. It is also relevant because we now know that the mechanism of life is made of non-living crystals.

A native stands before the airliner – a native who has only recently been introduced to metals and smelting. The white man, impatient at the native's refusal to believe in the white man's aeroplane factories, ironically dismisses the native's curiosity by saying "This is how the airliner originated. One day there was a terrific thunderstorm. Lightning played upon ore-bearing rocks, and fused the various ores into lumps of molten iron, copper and bauxite. Again the lightning struck before the metals had cooled, so that the metals formed themselves into patterns inherent in their atomic particles. This resulted in simple components being formed – nuts, bolts, aluminium plates, etc. Again the lightning struck and formed more complex components – cylinder heads, pistons, rings, wires (ready insulated), turbines, blades, propeller parts, wheels, and melted some rubber trees into tyres and left all these in a heap.

"Again the lightning struck and flung the heap high into the air. Some of the nuts were near enough to the bolts to respond to an inherent attraction and screw themselves together capturing another component in the process and so were selected for the developing plane. Other pieces fell uselessly as unwanted debris and so were not selected. After repeated lightning the major units were formed: engines, panel instruments, struts, fuselage, tanks, seats and lavatory pans.

"Coincidentally an earthquake ruptured the strata and released oil from an anticline. The oil spouted and poured itself into the tanks, refining and separating into grades on the way.

"A final burst of lightning flung everything up into the air. There were far more parts than those required by any one aeroplane, but those which were lucky enough to fall into a viable position made up a complete airliner which throbbed into life and made a safe landing."

This was the kind of explanation which was offered by Oparin, the Russian Communist scientist, and by Bernal and Urey. The component products for life's essentials were amino-acids and protein. The formation of these into living organisms was postulated through lightning repeatedly playing upon a rich hot soup of hydro-carbons and ammonia, upon the surface of the primeval ocean some 4,000 million years ago. This resulted in amino-acid soup which eventually formed into proteins, which are complex. Such explanations convinced some people, especially when they made laboratory experiments and produced a few amino acids in a vessel containing hydrocarbons, ammonia and water, charged by electricity.

Then snags became apparent. The amino acids were seen to be merely the building blocks of protein, equivalent to the lumps of molten ore in our illustration. These exhibited no order or pattern, yet the production of a protein required many hundreds of amino acids aligned in specific order, and this was for *only one* requisite protein-pattern among many others required.

Meanwhile, the scientist, like the native of our illustration, had been ignoring the existence of the factory which produced life. The existence of the factory was becoming more of a reality. Watson and Crick had unravelled the DNA code which controlled it. They now had to explain the origin of the cell as a factory. Bernal says "Cells appear as multiple factories with a complex economy of their own."[4]

The completion of the cell factory must have been brought about, it was thought, at least by 4,000 million years ago, which was not very long after the origin of the Earth. This imposed the problem of insufficient time available for such a major assemblage of mechanisms. Bernal frankly admits such problems: "Even such a basic mechanism as photosynthesis, which of necessity must have come near the beginning, involves mechanisms in the chloroplasts themselves requiring the formation of dozens of specific enzymes."[5] (*Origin of Life*, p. 137) Chloroplasts in plant life were an early development.

The New Guinea native did not believe in white man's factories. He would probably be just as likely to reject the ironic explanation, if the white man had made it, of the origin of the product. In any case the natives thought out their own theory which accorded more with their beliefs. They formulated the "Cargo Cult". They could not believe the white man was cleverer than the spirits of their ancestors. So to them the explanation was plain to see. The ancestor spirits had dispatched these aeroplanes with cargoes for the benefit of their protégés, but the wicked white man had intercepted and confiscated them and used them to their own ends.

Unhappily, so simple an explanation is not available for scientists as regards the factories of life. As the terms used in molecular biology are many and technical, we shall continue to use the terms of our analogy to unfold the problem. In the succeeding pages we shall consider the following problems:

The origin of the cell factory; the origin of the cell's computer tapes and code; the origin of the copy-typists; the origin of the thousands of machine operatives and their 200 trades; the origin of the shop floor machinery and assembly line; the origin of the Ministry of Fuel and Power; and the origin of the mechanism to reproduce further factories and firms.

It is easier to take the first two points together – *the factory and the code*. Dr. Graham Chedd reporting said that the knowledge we have of life's mechanisms "begs one key question. How did the mechanism which

[4] J. D. Bernal, op. cit., p. 155.
[5] Ibid., p. 137.

allowed subsequent evolution itself evolve?"[6] When it became apparent that both factory and code needed explanation, it was considered whether the product had produced the factory. Was it possible that the product – which in our analogy was the airliner – had left a record in its associate materials, of how another airliner could be produced, or did the factory fall together first, or was it that the code-words floated around and doodled until they linked up after producing isolated machine parts? In other words, did code-words spelling out, for instance, nut, bolt and strut, produce the isolated things named, and, being attached to their products, link up to make sentences, and so on, until by selection there were several books produced on how to manufacture a whole airliner?

This is an analogy of the explanation offered by Crick and Orgel to explain the big problem of the two different materials used.[7] As one could not have developed from the other, they suggest that bits of both developed together. If their suggestion were a possibility there would still be the *problem of the origin of the copy-typist*. Without her there would be no instructions to feed into the machines – the machines which manufacture protein. But the copy-typist is made of protein and so needed to be made by the machines, but the copy-typist could not be made by the machines without copy-typists already in existence to replicate the copy instructions for the machines. It has been suggested, therefore, that the first copy-typists were made of nucleic acids and not amino acids. There is no evidence for this, and it seems unlikely that evolution would overcome its first major problems in one material, and having done so successfully, switch to a different material; and we have no enzymes in nature made of nucleic acid.

"There is an additional problem in a system based on nucleic acids alone. Even given a mechanism whereby they could copy themselves, the most that such a system could indulge in would be (to use Orgel's graphic phrase) 'replicative doodling'. Before they can 'come to life' they must be able to modify their environment, and make use of the chemicals available there. In short they must be able to act as catalysts. And the only known biological catalysts are proteins."[8]

It is to this problem that Crick and Orgel turn their attention. Orgel points out a great stumbling block. To maintain any degree of order, the polypeptides (i.e. the string of aminoacids making up the protein) must be capable of producing identical copies of themselves. And no mechanism is known by which polypeptides can replicate in the absence of nucleic acids. On the other hand no nucleic acid (either DNA or RNA) is able to replicate itself without proteins to act as catalysts. These facts do not prevent the authors from resorting to sheer imagination and wishful

[6] Graham Chedd, "Crick on the Origin of the Code", *New Scientist*, January 23, 1969.
[7] Crick & Orgel, "Origin of the Code". *Journal of Molecular Biology*, Vol. 38, p. 367.
[8] Ibid., p. 174.

thinking to convince themselves that, contrary to the facts, certain things could have happened.[9]

Thus the origin of the master-tape still seems to be the major problem. When the close analogy between the DNA strand of the cell and punched tapes feeding instructions into automated machines was pointed out to a certain computer expert, he said, "The instructions to be coded on the tapes are worked out by our experts in the Logic Department, but who designed the logic of the master-copy in the cell?"

It was explained to him that some thought code-words were jostled about until the nonsense dropped out and sentences formed, which became logical and highly technical instructions for building machinery then through a series of copyist errors which sometimes led to an improvement which would be selected, the machinery they were able to produce would become increasingly complex. The expert looked quite incredulous and said that in the case of his factory, any error in the punched tapes could only be deleterious.

He spoke then of the copy-typists' department, whose Flexowriters translated the alphabetic letters into the punch holes on the tapes, and of the Reproducers which copied the master-tapes. There seemed to be so many parallels between them and the cell's central office. When told that the genetic code had a capital codon AUG where an operation commenced, and a full stop UAA where the product was released, he said that the capital letter in their code was an "H": it was the starting point of a sentence and every stage in the operation must commence at an "H".

There was great excitement in the scientific world when the capital letter and full stop of the DNA code were recognized in May, 1966. Dr. Peter Stubbs reported "So rapidly does understanding of the genetic code advance that not only is the full set of code-words now essentially buttoned up, but the molecular biologists are actually beginning to spot the punctuation marks that start and end the messages which a gene sends to the cell's protein factories, the ribosomes. Last year a code word signifying the 'full stop' or 'end of message' was discovered by Dr. S. Brenner and his colleagues at the Medical Research Council's Laboratory for Molecular Biology, Cambridge. On May 5, Dr. Francis Crick, also of the MRC Laboratory, told the Royal Society in his Croonian Lecture that the Cambridge workers had now discovered a code word that appeared to be a 'capital letter' initiating the message."[10]

In man-made computer-controlled factories there are three codes in use. They are called ISO, EIA and KDF. In the genetic code there is only one. The DNA code is universal throughout all life on earth from bacteria and plants to man.

[9] F. Crick and Orgel, "Origin of the Code", *Journal of Molecular Biology*, pp. 367, 381.
[10] P. Stubbs, "Reading the Genetic Code", *New Scientist*, May 12, 1966.

"All of our present knowledge about the genetic code indicates that it is universal," writes Graham Chedd, "and that a triplet that codes for the amino acid alanine in a bacterium will also code for alanine in a fly, a man, a silver birch or a stickleback."[11]

The DNA code is more economical in its use of signs. It needs only four because they are interpreted in triplets. This in effect gives 64 possible letters (some call them three-lettered words). The punched tapes by contrast need 48 different signs for the 42 letters, numbers and punctuations. In the DNA code the 64 groups of three letters are called codons, and 61 of them code for a particular amino acid. According to the order of the codon-letters, the order of amino acids is produced, and according to the order in the chain of amino acids, perhaps 3,000 of them, a particular protein is produced, and the protein becomes perhaps a hair, or a heart valve or an enzyme to catalyse production.

G. Beadle, the Nobel Prizewinner in Genetics, describes the fantastic accuracy of the cell's copying mechanism by comparing it with the average number of errors made by copy typists. A battery of typists would have to copy half-a-million pages in those ten thousand volumes. They would have to copy them twenty times (as the cell does), and this would be equivalent to ten million pages. Each chapter of the tape has about 20,000 turns or helical twists in it. The strand is split at the point where it is being copied, and rejoined by another enzyme typist. Instead of taking days to do this, the cell does it in seventy-three seconds.

Of course, it is only the copy-typing made for the second method of cell division that will pass on characteristics to the progeny. We likened this to the amalgamation of firms. Upon the accuracy of the copies made rests the well-being of successive generations. It is only then that changes in species could take place through copying errors.

Beadle demonstrates that if a typist made one typographical error every twenty pages, this would produce 500,000 errors in ten million pages, representing one human being, yet if we take the frequency of a mutation – which is a copy error in the DNA code – this would be in comparison only ten errors in ten million pages. Most of those errors would not be passed on, as they would be shielded by the dominant gene in the duplicate copy, though recessive genes are a danger in close-relative marriages. Others would cause genetic death, and so would not be passed on to the human race, especially if it were the dislocation of a whole "sentence".[12]

Take the following sentence as an illustration: "The DNA code is an engineering text-book".

If the typist mistakenly places the fingers one letter to the right of where they should be, this would produce the nonsense phrase:

"Yjr FMS vpfr od sm rmhomrrtomh yrcy¾nppl."

[11] G. Chedd, *New Scientist*, November 30, 1967; p. 534.
[12] G. Beadle, *Language of Life* (Gollancz, 1967).

A misplacement like this is very rare in the DNA, but when it occurs, the biological result of a completely garbled message is genetic death.

Very infrequently a mutation, which only affects one letter (or amino acid), may prove beneficial. In malaria-infested countries the sickle cell mutation enabled human beings to resist malaria, though it made them anaemic, and so they survived where others died. In other words, those with this mutation were selected by the environment. However, in the case of sickle cell anaemia the infant mortality rate is 40 per cent and the fitness of survivors is greatly reduced. Sickle cell anaemia was the result of only one letter misspelt.

This knowledge of genetic inheritance changed Darwin's theory concerning the mechanics of evolution. Darwin thought that an animal could develop characteristics in its lifetime in its response to environment – say, that an elephant's trunk could lengthen so that he didn't need to stoop (if caught bending he might be attacked). Darwin thought that such alterations could be recorded in what he called "gemmules" and that these gemmules modified the offspring accordingly. It turned out that there were no such things as gemmules.

But the genetic experiments of Mendel the monk, ignored for forty years, were rediscovered in the early twentieth century, and were later developed by De Vries and others. Consequently for anthropologists the study of genetics has largely replaced the study of external measurements. We now know that the characteristics recorded in the DNA strands cannot be changed by any external factors in the life of the animal. All that environment can do is to select some characteristic already in the DNA code which makes the animal more suited to its environment. Thus only changes by errors in the genetic code, the language of life, can get passed on.

If for example, a typist copied the instruction "Make a bold man", but omitted the letter "b" in "bold"; the instruction would read, "Make a old man". The effect would probably be harmful to the product, resulting probably in a weak man instead of a strong man. (This is an oversimplification by way of illustration).

Most replications of genetic faults are harmful, and bring either extinction or disease, but could occasionally prove helpful. For if, on the other hand, the wisdom of an old man (though weak) kept him from the fool-hardy dangers of a bold man, it might result in a better chance of his survival.

What the materialist wants us to believe is that an *improved* animal could arise through a series of such copyist errors, without the corrections or improvements of a Supernatural Author. Mere variety would be insufficient to cause evolution, as the requirement is for higher orders and improved animals. The problem is whether random evolution unaided by a higher intelligence could produce this through copyist errors selected by environment.

Supposing typists kept typing out copies of a single 500-page book on the Mechanics and Construction of an Outboard Motorboat, the atheist wants us to believe that as the typists go on repeatedly recopying, their selected errors would gradually change the book into increasingly high technical instructions for building, say, a Nuclear Submarine, the instructions having developed, say, into 50,000 pages contained in 100 books. These books could represent for the purpose of an illustration, the chromosomes, though fewer in number, for the materialist has never explained how these various animals have come to have their instructions organized into a different number of volumes for classes of animals by mere chance. Even Bernal admits the appearance of programming,[13] but because his Marxism must not admit the existence of a programmer, he calls it "prescription", which he contends does not involve knowledge of the final product. But such an exercise in semantics is merely verbal camouflage.

So, genetically, the crunch for the materialist is this. He believes that instead of these copyist errors developing into a book of complete nonsense as one might have supposed, the language would assume more and more what we would expect from the world's cleverest brains. The instructions for making a sea urchin would increase in size and technology to give precise instructions for making a man.

Really, with the directives of a higher intelligence excluded, the theory is little better than those apes banging away on typewriters to produce by accident Shakespeare's plays, but the theory is dressed up in more sophisticated terms.

The favourite example of the industrial moths is often advanced as an example of how a new species can arise by selection.

Soot-laden atmosphere blackened the surrounding countryside so that birds could detect only the light-coloured moths, and left the dark ones alone. So practically only dark moths exist today; thus a new type is supposed to have arisen. It is a misrepresentation to say they are a new type. They are the same both in appearance and genes as their ancestors. Only the white moths have disappeared through ineffectual camouflage.

The examples of bacteria which have become resistant to penicillin, and even to require penicillin, are in the same category. The environment may have selected a small change in the creature, but no experiment has produced a step-up in the order of life. These are only selections of the same level of life. Degeneration is the only process which has been established by experiment, or variety and elaboration in the same species.

More advanced creatures could come into being by chance, it is suggested, by faulty doubling of genes, or by recombination of chromosomes. No examples of this have yet produced a more complicated creature. The

[13] J. D. Bernal, *Origin of Life* (Weidenfeld & Nicholson, 1967), p. 167.

results have been only faulty reproduction in insects, such as the fruit fly, and in man, mental backwardness, for example, mongolism.

In fact, as Prof. Catcheside pointed out at Oxford, there is entropy, or "running down" to be taken into account. Mutations may be responsible for deterioration of a species rather than an evolutionary advance. Some regard bacteria and viruses as resulting from degeneration. They seem to have become incomplete in themselves, and need to invade and destroy other cells in order to complete their life-cycle. Genetic replication faults (mutations) could also be the cause of harmful parasites. Some protozoa also have become harmful to mammals through gene alteration. The DNA message would seem to have deviated. Mutations result from the faulty copying of instructions. Such faults are rare in such an accurate and complicated reproduction mechanism, but they can be increased by X-rays, gamma rays and other mutagens. How many such faults can a human race absorb before succumbing? A succession of earlier types of man have radiated to cover the old world and then have died out before our present race of *Homo sapiens* appeared. Was this because saturation point had been reached in mutations?

Prof. Alister Hardy said that by 1890 the scientist had convinced the world of the truth of chance evolution, but had come to know among themselves that the theory would not work. Then they were rescued by the theory of the mutation of genes.[14] But many biologists are coming to admit that this will not give an adequate mechanism for evolution either. Prof. Cannon says that the evolutionary development of a creature depends entirely on the appearance of new organs, limbs, functions, etc. These could never be produced by mutations, which can only modify organs that already exist. There is a very good chapter upon the inadequacy of present genetic theories to account for higher species, by Robertson and Sinclair (Iowa State University, and California University)[15] in a recent symposium produced by the American Scientific Affiliation. They refer to a statement by Dr. R. B. Goldschmidt who declared that present theories work only on the level of species, and are inadequate to explain the origin of higher categories.

We must not overlook the fact that connected with the problem of the origin of the DNA Code there are mechanical processes we should consider. These are connected with the *machinery of cell division and reproduction* without which life would never have progressed beyond the single cell stage. It is all very well to discuss the problem of making complete copies of the master DNA originals. But as involved as they are, they would remain useless without those mechanical horses to propel and reassemble each tape in the nucleus of the new cell. The single factory

[14] E. B. Ford, *Mendelism and Evolution*, Methuen, 1960, Preface to 6th ed.
[15] Robertson & Sinclair, *Genetics, Evolution and Christian Thought Today* Ed. R. L. Mixter Paternoster Press 1959) pp. 71–91.

would never become a firm, and two firms would never merge to become a syndicate. Higher forms of life would not be possible.

Until the second set of master copies has been produced the mechanical horses and winding gear remain inactive in the factory outside the office. In this state there would seem to be no natural cause to give rise to this mechanism essential to reproduction, and there have been no attempts to explain what would call it into being. Yet again, the mechanism is elaborate, and would appear to be programmed.

Then when we consider what could have originated meiotic division to make the merger possible, we are offered no explanation. How could the mechanism arise without supernatural planning when it is so utterly different from the first method, and so obviously essential for bi-sexual reproduction?

Meiosis can be defined as a mechanism whereby the chromosome number is reduced by half so that each female egg and male sperm has 23 chromosomes, in order that on fusion the full number of 46 chromosomes is restored, instead of their being doubled to 92 and doubled repeatedly with each generation.

This meiotic type of division has five substages added to its first stage, and each successive stage has consistent differences to carry through the operation. Meiosis assorts and recombines the genetic contributions of an individual's parents. C. Stern in "Principles of Human Genetics" compares it with the shuffling of a deck of cards. The recombining of genes in meiosis explains why each child of a couple has many genetic characters that other brothers and sisters do not possess. This means that no children in the world population, except identical twins, are likely to have exactly the same genetic characteristics as anyone else. In addition to physical variation, as well as group likenesses, it makes married life and family life possible, in which the young are educated and culture can develop.

We now leave the managerial office and go on to the factory floor. We find we have to consider the *origin of the machine operatives and their 200 specific trades*. Each of these 200 operations can be done only by the enzyme-robot who has the specific tools and training.

For this reason Crick postulates 200 "frozen accidents", which means that 200 times the right complex pattern formed itself into an enzyme and then became fixed at the right moment so that the pattern deviated no further. Crick admits that this is an extreme view (January, 1969) and is too accommodating.

It is indeed asking for 200 miracles. When Merrifield and Gutte produced a far simpler enzyme in their experiments in 1969 it required 12,000 separate operations for them to synthesise it, and it took three weeks (it takes the cell only ten seconds to do it!). In addition to such "happy accidents", Chedd points out[16] there are so many other happy accidents

[16] G. Chedd, "Crick on the Origin of the Code", *New Scientist*, January 23, 1969.

required, such as why only twenty amino acids out of those available should be used as the building blocks for all proteins made.

Crick thinks that at first only a few of the twenty amino acids would be evolved and used to make up a protein. If so, why are there no forms of life still in existence using this limited type of protein? All protein whether in bacteria, cabbages or man, use all the twenty amino acids as building blocks. The virus (or phage) which is considered to be at the borderline of life and non-life, codes for the same twenty amino acids, which again emphasizes the unity of life on earth in time and space, and it is the same DNA strand which codes for it. Did it issue from one patternmaker?

The solutions suggested seem quite inadequate to meet requirements, and there is the tendency to escape from the problem by verbal suggestions which beg one question after another. Such arguments are paramount to lifting oneself by one's own bootlaces. Take the following as an example: "As this 'bootstring' process continued, more amino acids being made use of and the coding process becoming more sophisticated, the proteins made would have become susceptible to further coding changes."[17]

All this is so easy to say, and yet there are a thousand-and-one improbabilities wrapped up in those glib words. Yet one finds so many who are uncritically convinced should one of the thousand requirements be shown to be possible by an experiment, thus taking it as proving the rest.

There is also another illogical tendency. It is frequently accepted that if man can reproduce in the laboratory one of the units of life, this demonstrates that it could have happened by accident in the first place. It would be more logical to conclude that because the assemblage required the intelligence of man, the original appearance of life required supernatural intelligence – supernatural because as the natural had not yet appeared, its origin must be of higher order than natural.

We know much of the mechanism of life now. It is a matter of finding a tool-kit minute enough to assemble the complex machinery. When scientists are able to do this, it should not lessen our awe at the Creator's wonderful skill. Indeed it should enhance it, for it will have taken the world's best brains to discover the mechanism and to copy it.

Some are frightened at the thought of scientists producing life. They whisper in hushed voice, "One day they will make life, and then what will happen to religion?" There is no logic in this reaction. It is like a GPO engineer who learns all the techniques of sending a cablegram, and because the mystery is removed through his learning the trade, declares he no longer believes in the existence of Henry Morse who invented telegraphy, and sent the first message under the ocean which was: "What God hath wrought!"

Hearn and Hendry say, "Even the simplest forms of life we know today

[17] Ibid.

seem to use the same types of huge protein molecules as catalysts" as more complex forms of life do.[18]

This highlights the difficulty of explaining the origin of catalysts and enzymes without supernatural agency. Concerning it, even Oparin and others are becoming more frank. In a talk at Birkbeck College he said that in his mind the most difficult question is how enzymes first came into existence. "An enzyme's structure is adapted in a very specific way to the particular catalytic task it must carry out in intact living systems; but it is just this appearance on the scene of adaptiveness in the simple aqueous solution of the primeval broth *before* the formation of such whole systems, that seems entirely improbable."[19]

He postulates droplets which he calls "protobionts" floating upon the primeval ocean, and breaking up into daughter droplets under the influence of wave-action. Once this happened, "prebiological natural selection" could operate. Others would deny the possibility of pre-biological natural selection. Here again is an example of accounting for complex results by an inadequate cause. The suggested wave-action sounds rather like Gen. 1:3. "The Spirit of God moved upon the face of the waters." Here is wave-action plus an adequate cause. The materialist's difficulty is that enzymes, even if formed, are very unstable and would last only a few minutes unless there were present all the other machinery to perpetuate and reproduce.

Next we must consider the machines which the enzyme robots use. The attempts to account for the *origin of the shop-floor machinery* and assembly line are no more adequate.

These ribosome machines select the various building blocks (amino acids) and assemble them into proteins or enzymes. Even the simple bacteria has 15,000 ribosome machines on its shop floor.

Each assembly line consists of a number of machines through which the code instructions of the Messenger RNA tape are fed. A second RNA translates the code into the three-letter words which describe the amino acid required. The enzyme robot then recognizes the correct amino acid and plugs it into position on the assembly line. When the full stop enters the ribosome, the machine releases the completed protein, which is called a peptide. Around each machine is gathered a supply of amino acids and robots ready to identify and plug in the building block for which they are responsible.

We mentioned that there were departmental foremen which controlled and co-ordinated output. They are those who ensure that any one department is constructing the correct section in the overall plan.

Dr. Kendrew of Cambridge wrote of problems yet to be solved,

[18] Hearn & Hendry, The Origin of Life, *Evolution and Christian Thought Today*, Ed. R. L. Mixter (Paternoster Press, 1959), p. 62.
[19] A. I. Oparin, *New Scientist*, June, 1967.

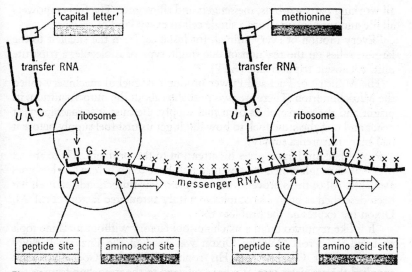

Fig. 18: Machinery in our cells: Ribosomes and an RNA assembly line. Both the "capital letter" and methionine are carried by a transfer-RNA that can plug into the codon AUG. However, the capital letter transfer-RNA can only fit into the peptide site, while methionine transfer-RNA can only fit into the amino acid site. When AUG occurs at the beginning of the messenger-RNA it first appears in the peptide site, so the capital letter slots in. When the AUG codon occurs in the middle of the messenger it first appears in the amino acid site, so that methionine fits in.

"What mechanisms of molecular control switch the appropriate genes 'on' or 'off', not only to make the right kinds of tissue but also to produce them in the right places?" He adds "We can only guess at the intricacy of the molecular control mechanisms that we shall one day find to be involved."[20]

We see here a combination of factors all dependent upon each other for the successful and accurate completion of their task. Is it possible that this machine shop had no architect or construction engineer? If all the bits and pieces were strewn around, could they be assembled by chance and natural selection? A factor to be remembered is that the enzyme workers die within a few minutes unless sustained. They, as well as the copy-typists, are made of protein; protein is made by the ribosomes. Here is the impasse again. The ribosomes need the robots already in existence before they can make the robots!

Other machinery in the cytoplasm's workshop has not been mentioned, but we have referred to *the problematic origin of the Ministry of Fuel and Power*. Machinery cannot work without fuel. This energy is supplied to

[20] J. C. Kendrew, *The Thread of Life* (Bell, 1966).

all working parts – robots, messengers and ribosomes. The fuel empowers all life and movement, from a single cell to every kind of creature.

"Every motion of every animal, for instance, from the smallest to the largest, relies on the reaction of one single type of molecule, a tripartite unit, adenosine triphosphate (ATP)."[21]

The Ministry of Fuel and Power produces its fuel in machinery called the Mitochondrion. There are two problems about the mitochondrion, its origin and the source of its own fuel supply. Because it is machinery, it needs and uses the same fuel, so how did it get its first fuel supply before it had manufactured a supply?

Prof. Malcolm Dixon gives his attention to this problem. There are six processes through which the raw materials have to go before fuel becomes available. All of these processes are complex. The mitochondrion itself has been described as being as complex as a fully automated factory. Prof. M. Dixon has expressed the problem thus:

"It is like trying to build a machine-tool factory without machine tools to build it." Prof. Malcolm Dixon was head of the Enzyme-Biology Department at Cambridge.[22] His conclusion is that God must have supplied the requirements. We have referred to the mitochondrion as the Ministry of Fuel and Power, inferring that the system has an autonomy of its own. Each mitochondrion has its own DNA and so is a separate ministry independent of the all-powerful Central Control of the Factory Management.

This has raised questions about the origin of the mitochondrion. Was it a bacterium which the cell adopted – a form of symbiosis – if so, from what source came the cell's fuel before? Some suggest the peroxisomes – but what before that? This only pushes the problem farther back and in any case gives no solution to the origin of the fuel for the first mitochondrion's own machinery before it had come into production?

So the mitochondria join the other problematic units in the materialist's endeavour to account for the appearance of life. The DNA nucleic thread depends upon a protein copy-typer which it cannot produce. The ribosome manufacturing machines are without attendant robots to work the machinery because it is the machinery which makes them, and because no copy-tape instructions can come through from the management. And all await the delivery of fuel which the mitochondrion cannot produce because it has none to work its own refinery!

To return to our analogy; it looks as if we have gone too far in breaking down the airliner and, indeed, its factory. In the attempts to avoid the need for a designing engineer, theorists have broken down the machinery into non-functional units. The inert heaps, like the theories, are fit only for the scrap-metal merchant.

[21] J. D. Bernal, *New Scientist.*
[22] M. Dixon and E. C. Webb, *Enzymes* (1958) p. 666.

CHAPTER XIV

THE "SIMPLE-TO-COMPLEX" FALLACY

TEILHARD DE CHARDIN IS BEING AVIDLY READ TODAY. HIS LAST
works were finished as long ago as 1947, and many of them were
written up to forty years ago. He said that at the very beginning
there was unresolved simplicity. He could certainly not say that today.
Most branches of Science have gained considerable data which have greatly
modified theories. As G. Chedd says, "In the 1920's the cell was a simple
uncomplicated thing."[1] This led to concepts which were hazy and dis-
tinctly unsatisfactory. Protoplasm was thought of as a primordial slime in
which the properties of life mysteriously resided.

Some determined materialists are still so obsessed with the simple to
complex outlook that they mislead both themselves and others by describing things as simple when they are not. In a debate with the author before
the Durham Anthropological Society,[2] Dr. Crosby parried the force of the
argument that proteins had complex strings of many hundreds of amino
acids, by saying that lengths of railway line make up a main-line hundreds
of miles long, yet the lengths are still simple. In so saying he missed the
whole point. It is not a matter of whether the amino acids are simple or
not. It is a matter of there being twenty types which are arranged in a
precise pattern for each protein. One amino acid out of place would alter
the character of the material produced. Moreover, the type of protein is
not haphazardly produced. Enzyme robots in co-ordination with co-
enzymes, RNA and ribosomes, empowered by ATP, are dedicated to
turning out their own particular protein. It does not seem logical to assume
that a product which can only be manufactured by complex machinery
could have come into being originally by simple processes without that
machinery!

There are many scientists who are ready to admit that the matter of
origins is beyond the scope of science, whether it be of matter or of life.
Ultimately, it should be admitted that the real problem is a philosophical
one.

Prof. Sir Bernard Lovell said in his Reith Lectures on the subject of
astrophysics: "If I were pressed on this problem of creation, I would say
that any cosmology must eventually move over into metaphysics for
reasons which are inherent in modern scientific theory." And again, "It
seems to me unlikely that there can ever be a scientific description, whether
in terms of the evolutionary or steady-state theories." And further: "We

[1] G. Chedd, *New Scientist,* June 27, 1968.
[2] February 4, 1969.

begin to cross the boundaries of physics into the realms of philosophy and theology."[3]

Science is able to formulate theories only about what can be observed. Hoyle can take back the business of origins no further than matter in his modified steady state theory. We cannot accept that matter is eternal because one then has to ask who or what made matter? It is just as philosophical as the question "Who made God?" It is only the existence of "nothing" which raises no problems, but where something exists, then human reason requires an explanation. But are there some things which exist that are beyond the ability of the human mind to comprehend? Time would seem eternal and space for ever and ever without end. Is supernatural mind or spirit in this category? Einstein's theory of the curvature of space-time seems to work in practical physics, but few could sum up a mental image of it. As Sullivan said, "The scientific universe is more mysterious than it has ever been before in the history of thought."[4] Is it therefore logical to theorize as if all existence can be observed within the limits of our five senses?

The outlook of anthropology was also one of some simplicity when Teilhard de Chardin was writing. It was thought that the present Western races had developed from the long-headed half-stooping Neanderthal man. It was not realized that he had a worldwide radiation. He was thought only to have occupied the caves of Europe. He, in turn, was supposed to have developed from something like Piltdown man with apelike jaw – the fraudulent concoction.

Piltdown man was linked somehow with Heidelburg apeman from the jaw section discovered in Germany (now classified as a *Homo*). Before him was fitted in "Dawn Man" whose construction was founded upon that discovery of a single tooth, which was later rejected.

No one knew for sure what the next ancestor was, whether he came from Asia or from the African fossils who were regarded as well on the way to the Ape-man.

As for Australian aboriginals, they were regarded as descended from Pekin ape-man or China ape-man, who was flat-headed and thought to walk with a pronounced stoop.

The peoples of the East were thought probably to have developed from Java ape-man. Both China and Java ape-men are now reclassified as *Homo erectus*, i.e., erect-walking man.

There were, of course, variants on this scheme, but this was the general picture. In turn all these supposed ape-men were descended from apes, and they from monkeys, and they from the tree-climbing lemurs of Madagascar, and they from the little owl-eyed tarsiers, and they from the

[3] A. C. B. Lovell, *The Individual and The Universe*, BBC Reith Lectures (Oxford, 1958) pp. 91, 95, 109, 110.
[4] J. W. N. Sullivan, *Limitations of Science* (Pelican), p. 89.

THE "SIMPLE-TO-COMPLEX" FALLACY

small rat-like tree-shrews. As has been said above, anthropologists now see that none of the above creatures developed directly from each other.

This, however, fitted in with the general evolutionary picture of mammals from monotremes and monotremes from marsupials like the animals of Australia and Southern South America which bear their young in a pouch. Again there are no connecting fossils between these orders. Further back along the line were reptiles, amphibians, and then the first backboned marine animals, the fish. Before them it was assumed in spite of a large fossil gap that the marine animals without backbones were their ancestors. Of these there were about nine classes called phyla. Their first fossils were laid down in the Cambrian seas then dated as 500 million years ago, but because these were already complex and appear together without any evolutionary tree, it was assumed there had been evolution of soft-bodied creatures for three times that amount of time before, namely 2,000 million years, which had left no fossils. These in turn had developed from that simple piece of jelly called protoplasm.

The inorganic world was also regarded as basically simple. The simplest atom being merely a proton and electron. Dr. R. E. D. Clark says, "By the end of the 1920's things were settling down again. A new simplicity seemed on the way – at least for those who could shut their eyes to the more disconcerting discoveries that had been reported. The universe was made of electricity. It contained only negative and positive charges. Given space and electric charges, the chemical elements would form automatically and their properties would follow as a matter of course. Nature was so simple that, perhaps, it obeyed just one simple equation and, when man had found it, the days of mystery would be ended. . . . Once again there followed, in the thirties, a welter of new discoveries and they have come thick and fast ever since. Though we cannot, as yet, with any certainty, link them with Christianity, it can hardly be questioned that the general tenor of discovery falls into line with Christian expectations."

As Clark says, "We have now progressed a long way since the early part of the century when it was supposed that there were only two kinds of matter – electrons and protons," and "The quite staggering complexity of life is to be contrasted with the extreme simplicity of the 'protoplasm' envisaged by atheistic writers in the nineteenth century."[5]

Teilhard de Chardin could not write now as he did in 1947 concerning the evolution of matter: "At the very bottom there is an unresolved simplicity. . . ."[6] Of course he could see that even this would not account for the ascending atomic scale of complexity without supernatural "within-ness", as he called it, but he could not speak of simplicity today. Complex particles, ranging from Alpha to Omega, have been

[5] R. E. D. Clark, *The Christian Stake in Science* (Paternoster Press, 1967), pp. 60, 62, 137.
[6] P. Teilhard de Chardin, *The Phenomenon of Man* (Collins, 1959), p. 52.

discovered interacting within the machinery of the once supposedly simple atom.

These exciting discoveries of the complexity of matter have been made particularly during the last few years.

Professor P. T. Matthews, F.R.S., wrote in February, 1964, "February should go down in the history of physics as the time when a new fundamental law was established. The frontier of physics has lain, since the war, in the field of sub-nuclear particles. There have been spectacular advances, each five-year period producing a new and quite unexpected development."[7] He said that this month a coherent pattern was emerging to bring order and beauty into this sub-nuclear world which had been becoming more complex and confused. There were now between fifty and a hundred semi-stable sub-nuclear entities controlling the interaction of protons and neutrons. He predicted, on the grounds of mathematical calculations of Gellmann and Ohnuki, the existence of a particle called omega-minus, which has quite extraordinary properties.

Within a week of this article Omega-minus was discovered by a team of thirty-three physicists headed by Dr. R. P. Shutt of Brookhaven, showing how the particles fit together into "Families" with an elegant symmetrical pattern according to their physical properties.

This was the confirmation of the new theory of Unitary Symmetry in strong interactions – a dramatic advance in the understanding of the laws of nature.

Since then, discovery has gone on apace. Over 200 particles have now been discovered, and also other forms of matter such as antimatter, neutrinos, etc., which are of a character which could suggest the connexion by which the spirit world controls matter.

A similar sort of connexion biologically was made by Sir Alistair Hardy, a former President of the Royal Society. He brings another dimension into biology – that of consciousness. "Consciousness cannot be explained in two dimensions; the phenomenon of cells working together in co-operation is not explained. For example in *foraminifera*, which have no nervous system, cells work to a plan. Have they a psychic blueprint? Chemistry and biology do not give the full picture of reality."[8]

When we consider the non-solid nature of the atom, and that matter is a complicated interaction of forces within nothingness, so to speak, it suggests the unreality of matter and the reality of unseen forces, or the spirit world. It appears that unseen forces find it necessary to establish a very complex system of unseens in order to make matter. Matter, so to speak, is not easily come by. This new insight should prove to be the antithesis to materialism, and would argue that the basis of reality must be a spiritual one and that matter is but a medium of expression of the

[7] P. T. Matthews, "Alpha to Omega", *New Scientist*, February, 1964, No. 379.
[8] Sir A. Hardy, *Psychophysical Lecture* (Oxford, 1964).

unseen supernatural. Indeed material appearance is deceptive, to the naked
eye at least, of the real nature of things. For example your apparently
motionless solid stone wall is actually a seething mass of movement
of two kinds in empty space – the spin of protons and particles at
speeds approaching light and the mad jig of molecules which we call
temperature.

Even as late as 1962 some complex things were still being described as
simple. The mitochondrion, which we have described as the Ministry of
Fuel and Power, was described then as "a simple particle discernible in the
cell."

Upon this conception of the simple to the complex, Teilhard built his
religious philosophy, with Christ as the "Omega Point", as he named it.
It was a noble conception of a devotedly spiritual man well versed in the
science of his day, but it was built upon a false foundation. That Christ is
the future head and objective in the purpose of the Universe, is still valid,
but not that this is a naturalistic process of simple to the complex. We
shall consider a modern interpretation in our last chapter.

In the former chapter we saw how the materialistic theories of the
origin of life were fit only for the scrapheap because they had broken
down the units into non-functional bits, so that the atheist J. D. Bernal
frankly admits, "It would be easier to discuss how life didn't originate
than how it did."[9]

Since 1964 attention has been given to what the simplest functional unit
of life could be. At what point do non-living atoms and molecules become
sufficiently organized as a working unit of life? What is the minimum
complexity requirement for viability? The simplest units of life are phages,
viruses and scrapie.[10] How simple are these? It would seem that the
simplest viable machine of life has to be very complex. Professor
Catcheside said in his Oxford University Lecture on the borderland of
living and non-living, that even the simplest virus had 50,000 amino acids
in its shell, 60 protein units and 6,500 nucleotides. Even so it was not functional without using the ribosomes of bacteria (*E. Coli*) which it needed to
invade. Bernal considers the virus and bacteria as degenerate, which would
leave the cell as the "simplest" fully functional unit.

The difference between living and non-living is one of organization
rather than of materials. This is why our argument does not rest upon a
supposed gap between the organic and inorganic. At the borderland of
life, phages can be frozen and unfrozen, viruses can be dried and stored,
and revitalized. The basic stuff of life is made up of non-living materials –
nucleic and amino acids, etc. – containing in code, how the animal is to be

---

[9] J. D. Bernal, *Origin of Life* (Weidenfeld & Nicolson, 1967).
[10] Scrapie is an organism which attacks sheep and goats, but is not now considered to be a
functional unit of life. Most of the evidence seems to point to its being a small protein fragment
from a disrupted cell and therefore not self-replicating.

made. Thus the biochemist and the geneticist have come together on the molecular level in analysing life, but the invention of the remarkable machinery and the assembly of it would appear to require a more adequate explanation than that offered by materialists.

We have seen that the simplest unit of life such as a virus contains the same type of genetic code, that this code is complex. This implies that the first simplest possible forms of life was also complex, so that the conception of utter simplicity in the beginning is a false one.

It should not be thought that the object of emphasizing the complexity of the smallest unit of life is in order to make our contention for the need of a Creator rest upon the argument that because life is so wonderful it must therefore have been created. This may be impressive to many, but our argument is based upon the impossibility of assembling complex machinery in a fully working unit by chance. To suggest that environment would select it, if it did, is begging the whole question of the original assemblage.

As Prof. Monod has stated, "Life is not one of its constituent parts but the whole interacting unit." Urey may have produced amino acids in his laboratory but these are only the raw materials used in the living machinery.

Many theists were ineffective in contending with atheists because they were misled by Schwann who said that life was a "vital essence" – a sort of non-material mystery. As Prof. Monod said when speaking on the BBC science series on the cell's control of its metabolism, "Life is the whole interacting unit, not a vital essence." After describing the interacting mechanism involved in the energy supply control of ATP and ADP he added "God the Father is a most excellent mechanical engineer."[11] A motor engine is not a throbbing, working unit until all its essential components are assembled. In the same way life's wonder consists in Him who assembled all the non-living components. Here is the significance of the borderland between living and non-living.

Even the Russian scientist, Oparin, admitted the following when he outlined the present state of the subject at Birkbeck College when Prof. Bernal was in the chair. The action of passing electric charges through reaction mixtures representing the "primeval soup" cannot exhibit, he said, "any great degree of organization".[12] By this he admitted the lack of an explanation for the assembly of components into machinery.

Oparin's conception that, given all the right conditions, life will inevitably arise, is the old fallacy that life originated by accident (called spontaneous generation) dressed up in a more philosophical language.

This revival of belief in spontaneous generation takes us back nearly one

[11] J. Monod, *What is Life?* (BBC Television Science Series, by Chedd & Goldwin, October 1968). Prof. Jacques Monod of the Pasteur Institute, Paris University, is a world authority on Life's processes.

[12] A. I. Oparin, Lecture at Birkbeck College. Reported in *New Scientist,* June, 1967.

hundred and twenty years to the arguments between Pasteur and his contemporaries.

Consequently some of our bacteriologists have become concerned, because it suggests lack of co-ordination between the disciplines (branches of science) for the whole science of bacteriology is founded upon the assumption that spontaneous generation never occurs.

Bacteriologists who work on the viruses and genes and the smallest viable units of life, could not carry out their experiments if there were any chance of life appearing in a sterile medium from nowhere. Yet, some "Origin of Life" biologists are working on the assumption that life can arise by chance.

Bacteriologists have 300 years' history of sound scientific experiment behind them in which at various times they have corrected by objective experiment the hasty claims of advocates of spontaneous generation. The story has a very familiar ring about it.

In the early days of the "Free thinkers" it was claimed that bad meat gave rise to life because fly maggots could be observed to appear on it from nowhere. It was in 1668 that Redi exposed the fallacy. He noticed that decaying meat not only produced flies but attracted them, so he put meat into small vessels. Some he sealed and some he left unsealed. The uncovered vessels bred maggots and the covered ones did not, as the flies were unable to reach the meat. It was thus proved that the flies originally laid their eggs in the decaying meat.

The next hasty claim for spontaneous generation was in 1675 when Leeuwenhoek invented lenses by which he was able to magnify water and broth. He observed that water developed protozoa in it after a time. He concluded that life arose automatically, for protozoa were minute transparent single-cell creatures visible only under a microscope. The conclusions from his sensational discovery were not corrected for over ninety years when in 1767 Spallanzani disproved it by boiling and sealing water and soup. When examined under a microscope it was seen to be free from protozoa and germs, or in other words it was sterile. He then boiled the water and left it open to the air, and later he found that it contained protozoa. Thus it must have been conveyed through the air.

Later in 1836 Schwann showed that life did not arise automatically in the air either. He sterilized the air and left a vessel of sterilized soup open in it. No protozoa or germs appeared in the soup. Schwann, however, led some scientists on a false scent in postulating that life was a vital principle, a non-material thing, instead of a wonderfully-made machine with observable materials.

The advocates of spontaneous generation, however, remained unconvinced, though they were unable to support their outlook with laboratory experiment. So, in 1860 the renowned Louis Pasteur demonstrated that germs were carried in the air by dust. He did this by putting a sterilized preparation in a globular container whose only outlet to the air was through a glass pipe which had a downward angle bend in it. In this bend the dust and particles of the air settled and failed to reach the preparation. The preparation remained sterile, thus showing that it was the dust particles in the air which carried these minute forms of life.

This exposure of the spontaneous generation theory prepared the way for Lister. Aseptic surgery, introduced by Lister, was now able to come into its own and save many lives. The need for sterility in the operating theatre had long been resisted as a result of the opposition by advocates of spontaneous generation.

If modern advocates of spontaneous generation have the advantage of sophistication, they have one severe disadvantage. They used to be able to say, "Given enough time the inconceivable can happen." We mentioned that it is openly admitted by Bernal and others that time is against them, and that for three reasons: First, the age of the earth now appears far too short for the odds of chance against the first step of life. Eugene Guy demonstrated mathematically that the earth has been in existence only a fraction of the time required for the formation of the first protein molecule. For a series of other chances to have taken place many more billions of years would be required, even granted that such things could happen.

Bernal admits the problem. "It is true that the mechanism applied to higher organisms is incredibly complex." The question was, "whether there would have been time for it in the 4·5 aeons" (4 thousand million years) since the origin of the earth. "Even such basic mechanism as photosynthesis, which of necessity must have come *near the beginning*, involves mechanisms in the chloroplasts themselves requiring the formation of dozens of specific enzymes."[13]

The second limitation is that the cell must have been in existence so early in earth's history, as to place evolution's biggest step in the shortest period. Bernal admits this, "Life in the last few thousand million years (this is long before the fossil record starts. E.K.V.P.), has become an extremely stable system. Biochemical evolution, except for bacteria, has virtually ceased."[14]

The third limitation, has been expressed by R. E. D. Clark. He demonstrates that co-enzymes and other necessary compounds remain stable for only half an hour, so that an expanse of time would not be available during which one complex accident could await others to join it in a workable unit. Before the first micro-organism could become viable, its first ordered moiety would fall apart again, or decompose, long before the rest were built up.[15] Jacob and Monod also make the point that messenger-RNA is inherently unstable, and can be quickly broken down and

[13] J. D. Bernal, *Origin of Life*, p. 137.
[14] Ibid., p. 135.
[15] R. E. D. Clark, *The Universe: Plan or Accident?* (Paternoster Press), p. 134.

replaced. Most bacterial messenger-RNA comes into this category, the average lifetime of the molecules at 37° C. being about two minutes.[16]

So then, in considering the possible causes for the origin of life, we cannot escape complexity at the outset either by playing for time or by pleading simplicity. The main basic difference in what we consider to be a more complex form of life higher up the scale is the complexity of the coded instructions of the DNA strand in the cells of modern animals. Most of the other units of the cell appear to have always worked with the same superb efficiency. With this observation the stage is set for the formation of a theory more adequate to meet the requirements of all these facts.

[16] Jacob and Monod, *What is Life* (BBC Television Science Series by Chedd & Goldwyn, October, 1968).

Fig. 19: An Analogy of the Cell's Automated Factory.

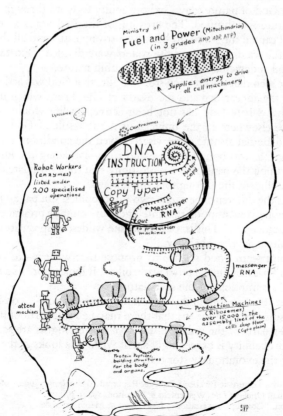

CHAPTER XV

THE NEED OF AN ADEQUATE THEORY

IN THE FORMER CHAPTERS WE HAVE BROKEN DOWN THE PROBLEM and demonstrated that cosmically speaking life could not have arisen at all. The limiting ideologies of materialists on the one hand have led to inadequate theorizing to account for complexity essential in the first unit of life. Now we must consider all the evidence from the various faculties of knowledge and reconstruct a workable hypothesis of how life arose and developed.

There has also been inadequate theorizing in some theological circles. There are those who prefer to believe that miracles are unrelated to the Laws of God in nature. A careful reading of the Bible, however, depicts God as the God of nature's laws, whose ability to work through His own laws of nature is unlimited. The crossing of the Red Sea is an example, "The Lord caused the sea to go back by a strong east wind all that night, and made the sea dry land, and the waters were divided" (Ex. 14:21).

Here God is depicted as being active within nature.

We have seen that the creation story implies that God was active within nature for the appearance and succession of Life. From which it may be assumed that where God has not been active, no life would appear. If there is life elsewhere in the universe it is the result of God's activity. Oparin and Bernal assume otherwise: "Given the conditions that existed at the time, life was bound to arise and to evolve along the lines that it has."[1] It is upon the basis of this philosophy that they postulate that there must be intelligent life throughout the universe.

Herein is the difference between two philosophies. On page 117 Bernal enlarges upon his assumption that intelligent life must be present elsewhere by chance, and ends, "This is, of course, the wildest of speculations, but it has a definite *a priori* probability..."[2]

It does not seem good science to propose that what is the *"wildest of speculations"* has a definite *a priori* probability! It looks more like reflecting the *a priori* assumptions of the speculators.

Professor H. Sandon in his "Cosmic Conversation"[3] considers the theory of some astrophysicists, that there may be some form of intelligent life in other parts of the universe. He says that biologists are sceptical of this. The probability is exceedingly small when one looks at the improbabilities of the evolutionary story on earth.

[1] A. I. Oparin, Lecture at Birkbeck College. Reported *New Scientist*, June, 1967.
[2] J. D. Bernal, *Origin of Life* (Weidenfeld & Nicolson, 1967), p. 117.
[3] H. Sandon, "Cosmic Conversation", *New Scientist*, March 31, 1966.

The effect of his thesis with its staggering figures, leaves the conviction which was not intended, namely that the story of life and man just could not have happened on earth any more than on any other planet unless there had been a supernatural agency.

First, he quotes other biologists on whether life elsewhere is feasible – the whole idea is "plainly false" says G. C. Simpson of America, and "incredibly improbable" says E. B. Ford the British geneticist.

Then he gives a list of the unlikely processes towards the first cell, and draws his first conclusion, "There is little doubt that the course of evolution which took place before the first cell appeared, was at least as long and difficult and as dependent on a sequence of improbable accidents as the whole of the subsequent evolution of the plant and animal kingdoms. Very many more of the theoretically habitable planets must have fallen out of the race long before getting so far." He adds, "Geological time may be long but it is short in comparison with the improbability of the sequence of accidents through which cells came into being."

Proceeding next to the fossil record of life after the first cell, he says, "Compared with the difficulties that had to be surmounted before the first fossils were formed, the subsequent steps in the evolution of the animal kingdom appear simple, but they are still incredibly improbable." He justifies that statement by a survey of the last 600 million years.

In conclusion he gives point to his "Conversation" by asking us to suppose that in the progress from primitive organic soup to modern industrialized man there were 100 critical steps, and that at each of these steps there were two possibilities. The odds against the final result would be 2^{100} to 1 (or a million, million, million, million, million to one!). But there were many more major steps than one in forty million years (which is the total of 4,000 million years of evolution divided by the 100 critical steps) so the actual odds were far greater.

The necessity of looking at the problem as it affected other possible planets, in a detached manner, should enable us to be more detached when viewing our own. It may enable us to consider a more likely cause and development of living organisms on earth, than the inadequate explanations of materialists. Life is not bound to arise merely because the right conditions are present, and the state of the other planets of our solar system shows that even the occurrence of the right conditions are not to be taken for granted.[4] The requirements of science and Genesis would be met by what might be called *Extra-cosmic* Coding and Re-coding. "Cosmic" refers to this cosmos in which we find order both in the physical and biological realm. We have seen that there are insufficient factors within matter and life to explain their origin or development. Therefore we must look outside the cosmos; hence the word "extra-cosmic".

The common feature of all living organisms is the DNA code. As there

[4] R. E. D. Clark, *The Universe: Plan or Accident* (Paternoster Press), Ch. 5–7.

is only one language used in it, the instructions must come from one source, and as the instructions for the simplest viable unit of life are complex, that source must be an adequate one with an intelligence equal to that required to invent a computer-automated factory. This code has been added to in the same grammar and vocabulary down – presumably – 4,000 million years, therefore the Being who is the source of that language must be constant and unchanging – not like those who speak human language, for a family of languages will change so much over the centuries that nations of common origin cannot understand one another.

If the creative source is not of the material things themselves, i.e., not of this cosmos, then it is not observable. As it is written "the things which are seen are not made by that which is visible" (Heb. 11:3). The source of the cosmos is therefore not available to empirical science through the normal five senses. Have we, then, other senses with which observation can be made such as prayer or telepathy? Or has that extra-cosmic source recorded evidence which can be observed by some of the five senses of man? It is conceivable that the extra-cosmic source might wish to communicate in human code to those who are the result of that source's genetic code. If so, then that communication should also be considered when theorizing on the origin of life.

Coding: Even the "origin of life biologists" cannot now conceive that the smallest piece of protein was independent of an equivalent piece of code instruction, so that coding was there at the beginning. They would say indeed, "In the beginning was the Code."

We have demonstrated that the smallest working unit of life could not be "bits" of the machinery, perhaps not even of something bigger like the virus, because it is not complete in itself but has to practise symbiosis with bacteria. Therefore the first code for the production of the simplest form of life must have been a DNA tape of considerable length. The subjects covered by chapters of technology must have been almost as many at the first appearance of life as with us, because all the basics of the machinery had to be coded for. It is only the elaboration of those chapters which has been the feature of what some call evolution.

Recoding: We have seen that the more recent knowledge of fossils demonstrates that the five main types of *Homo* are unconnected with each other. Likewise, our present race of *Homo sapiens* is unconnected with those other types before him. It is therefore assumed that there was a long line of "common ancestors" before *Homo sapiens* and before each of the other types, whose fossils have not been discovered.

The non-discovery of those fossils of common ancestors is in itself a difficulty, especially now that it is known that each of the known types of fossil-men had a worldwide spread, and was also associated with certain stone-tool cultures.

There are no tool cultures associated with any undiscovered and supposed common ancestor.

It would seem more reasonable to suppose that the DNA of the cells had been recoded for *Homo sapiens* at least. This would explain the common unity of Adam's cells with all other life. It would also explain the existence of specializations in the various earlier types of men, for it is these specializations which were not passed on to the other types which make anthropologists think that they could not be genetically linked in a linear fashion.

When we look at the fossil record of plants and animals we see a similar picture.

First we see this in some of the main divisions of life: Plants, Marine Invertebrates (without backbone), Marine Vertebrates, reptiles, birds and land animals and mammals. We also see this in the fact that most types of animals (phyla) first appear comparatively suddenly, and together, 600 million years ago in the Cambrian era. This last point holds good even if the single-celled fossil algae, 2,000 million years old, does prove to be real and not what is called a pseudo-morph. The fossil algae were discovered in the Canadian Gun Flint.

The appearance of all the major invertebrates in the Cambrian represents what has been called an explosion of evolution. If cellular life was already in existence it would be better described as a recoding of the cell for all the phyla. If however the cell was not in existence before then, it would represent the first coding. In any case it relates with Gen. 1:20, "Let the waters bring forth swarms of living creatures." God is represented as speaking or placing the code within marine life.

Next major recoding would be in the appearance of backboned fishes. There is no fossil record of what phyla gave rise to the vertebrates. Prior to their appearance thousands of fossils of every other branch of the animal kingdom have been preserved, but there is not one intermediate form. This sudden appearance of a radically new kind of animal, but with the basic cell-mechanism, has so far not been explained satisfactorily by either atheist or theist. A theory of recoding would solve the difficulties of this major advance.

Then the extensive changes embodied between cold-blooded egg-laying reptiles and warm-blooded placental mammals, would require a major recoding, unexplained satisfactorily by biologists. The remarkable mechanics of flight in birds would be another major recoding. It is a very clumsy suggestion of some that feathers, with their elaborate interlocking device, were a development from scales.

Finally, when man is created, the speech of God is again referred to: "Let us make man in our own image." The two sides to man's nature are distinct. His body comes from the earth like the animals, but his life, psyche, comes from God's breath.

Take first the sentence, "God formed man of the dust of the ground." The word "formed" implies a process. Was this a long process linking with Genesis 1 when the animals were also made of the earth? "God said, 'Let the earth bring forth the living creature'" (Gen. 1:24). Perhaps the words in the second chapter are a comment upon this, "Out of the ground the Lord God formed every beast of the field." Notice that the same verb "formed" is used. The word "formed" concerning man could be a comment upon his cellular ancestry, while the inbreathing of God – which is not said of the animals – could refer to man's spiritual nature by which he is distinguished from the animals.

Whatever philosophy we follow we must admit that man is different by having a spiritual awareness. He talks to an unseen God in prayer. Even if we think man is deluded in this, it is a strange difference. No animal even shows any consciousness of the need of prayer. What is the cause of this strange phenomenon causing millions of people throughout the world to give thousands of man-hours to thought-communication with a supposed Super-intelligence?

We have already seen that the explanations of the Victorian anthropologists have been admittedly inadequate.

If then the word "formed" links man's cells with the unity of all life, does the word "inbreathed" link with the statement of Chapter I, that God "created man in his own image"? The use of the verb "create" might indicate something more than recoding for man's spiritual nature, as the word is used very sparingly in Genesis 1. It appears only twice before – first when matter is created, and second when life emerges. Its equivalent in Genesis 2, "in-breathed by God", is even more distinctive. The spirit and breath are often synonyms in Scripture.

To return to physiology of man, we see that in any case God recoded for Eve's cells, because He would have to omit the "Y" chromosome from the cells He took from Adam's side, otherwise – to use an Irishism – Eve would have been another man.

The Psalmist said, "In God's book all my substance was written." The mysterious words of the Psalmist concerning his origin are well worth contemplating. One wonders what the Psalmist himself thought they meant:

> I will praise thee, for I am fearfully and wonderfully made;
>   Marvellous are thy works,
> And that my soul knoweth right well.
>   My substance was not hid from thee,
> When I was made in secret
>   And curiously wrought in the lowest parts of the earth
> Thine eyes did see my substance, yet being incomplete;
>   And in thy book all my members were written,
> Which in continuance were fashioned,
>   When as yet there was none of them (Psa. 139:14).

This translation was made in 1611 before modern science had really begun. So we can be sure the translation was not affected by modern concepts. Note those words "All my members were written."

The deciphering of the DNA code has revealed a language older than any human hieroglyphics, says George Beadle the geneticist and Nobel prizeman. It is "a language as old as life itself. Its words are buried deep in the cells of our bodies."[5]

If the code is as old as life itself, God must have recorded His instructions in the first functional unit of life, perhaps four thousand million years ago, or if not then, in view of the lack of fossil evidence, at least in the Cambrian 600 million years ago.

We have seen that the code system is thought to be universal throughout the realm of plant and animal life, and must have been present in the first workable unit of the life-machine. Hence when God spake in order to create life, what He said was recorded, not in punch-holes of a computer tape, but in a spiralling string of nucleic acids in a code. "God said, 'Let the waters bring forth life'" (Gen. 1:20). These instructions have been carried out ever since creation in every living cell "whose seed is in itself" (Gen. 1:11, 29). The instructions have a sufficient number of alternatives for living things to adjust themselves to their environment of climate and general ecology, or to specialize into their ecological niches.

Even the phrase "Dust of the ground" is not without its comparable statements today. Bernal and Oparin have some interesting remarks concerning life commencing in estuarine clays. Bernal, writing in 1967, said "I myself, suggested some years ago that another fairly obvious method is by the adsorption of these molecules on mineral particles, largely microcrystals, of clay or platy iron hydroxides, which could be found in a finely-divided state on beaches and particularly in estuaries. That is to say, I postulated the origin of the further condensations that were to lead to the origin of life as occurring not in open water but essentially in mud or soil."[6] Later he added another possibility – the agency of sea foam drifting on to estuarine clays. He develops the idea of life originating as a surface reaction on clay particles.

We are not necessarily agreeing with these opinions, but it should be a salutary lesson to atheist followers of Bernal who are all too willing to scoff at a similar statement in Scripture.

Bernal also quotes G. Mueller who has another variant. He thinks life might have arisen from cosmic dust.

If one wishes to obtain a realistic picture of the fossil history of life on earth, one needs to forget those nicely-drawn evolutionary trees of supposed fossil connexions. The long branches drawn to join a single stem are unrepresented by fossils and are the product of the imagination. Many

[5] G. Beadle, *Language of Life* (Gollancz, 1967).
[6] J. D. Bernal, op. cit., p. 57.

biologists in particular are unaware of how their idealized successions of genera are rehashed into what is regarded as being a feasible one from the evolutionary viewpoint. Often it is not the same order as that shown in the rocks. This is not an attempt to deceive. The fault is in the subjective habit of making everything bend to a theory.

When we look at the geological record of fossil life we find that much of it is a series of starts and stops, particularly among higher forms of life. We find this is confirmed in fieldwork. We examine a whole succession of rock systems extending through say 100 million years, and find this is confirmed. This is particularly so with monotremes, marsupials and mammals.

This does not mean that no changes and developments are evident in the fossil record of various families of animals. The picture presented is similar to that which we saw in the types of man or *Homo*, namely, a species appears to commence, then undergoes certain modifications and elaborations and then often becomes extinct. One has only to look at the interesting successions of sea-urchins, the name by which they are familiar to holiday makers. These echinoids are valued for their purple and blue half-football "shells", 5 inches in diameter, which are sold as ornaments. Their ancestors 500 million years ago were smaller and had very substantial differences. In this case they have not become extinct. But they were still echinoids.

An interesting example of adaptation is the marsupials of Australia and South America. These animals who carry their young in a pouch, have differentiated and filled many ecological niches which are occupied by their equivalent mammals in the Old World.

We have seen that the basic materials of life are the same and are composed of elements present in the cosmos. Likewise, there is a unity of life's mechanism. The basic sentences of the DNA coding are the same – hence all the bones in man's body have an equivalent bone in the frame of a horse.

The differences are in those parts of the DNA code which specify species' characteristics, and particularly the brain and stance of man.

Looking down the geological and palaeontological record of life's history there is definitely a connexion between all species, but the dissimilarities are as important as the similarities. In the past too much attention has been directed to the likenesses, called "homology", but as one views the palaeontological record as it really stands, there appear to be times of recoding; times when the Creator spoke afresh.

This is exactly what we find in the Genesis account. The expression "God said" or its equivalent occurs six times in reference to the progression of living orders of creatures. This would refer to acts of recoding. Between these acts, by adaptation these cellular-constructed creatures would go on, as expressed in the phrases "The waters brought forth abundantly after their kind" (Gen. 1:21), and, "Let the earth bring forth the living creature after his kind" (Gen. 1:24).

When a specialist has delivered a treatise or an author has written a book, it is easier to build up a larger book or revise a book than it is to rewrite it completely. Similarly, the physiological book of life housed in the cell has preserved the bones and structure of earlier books. Practically all the bones of the human skeleton are a repetition of those in animals and birds, except that they have been revised or recoded for different uses. It would be natural to retain the complex technical framework of a book of one million pages, such as that written in the cell.

This book which you are reading is another example. You may have noticed from the Preface that it is a development of a paper delivered to the Oxford Science Group, a department of the Student Christian Movement, which was further revised for the Southampton University Research Scientists' Christian Fellowship, a department of the Inter-Varsity Fellowship.

We have had an example in the spiritual book of life. The first three gospels are built upon the same framework of the Life of our Lord, but the three authors fit into the framework many other component parts of the Lord's life, using the same sentences, selected according to the events in the Lord's ministry they loved best. Finally, St. John supplemented the framework and material with personal knowledge of events and private matters which he had through living closest to the Lord.

Only when a theory needs radical alteration does a book need to be completely rewritten, such as Leakey's "Adam's Ancestors", when it was seen that the general theory of anthropology had developed upon wrong assumptions. Before that he had merely revised each edition.

So then the basic sentences and paragraphs in the physical book of life with their very technical details have been retained but have been reassembled into a different number of chapters for various species.

Among the numerous families and superfamilies of monkeys for instance, there is a considerable variation in their number of chromosomes.

For those inclined to accept uncritically a rather facile conception of evolution, they should reflect upon how radical is the reorganization of the chapters (chromosomes), especially when the alteration of one sentence, or even one word (an amino acid), can affect an animal so radically.

For those interested, the comparative anatomy of the human body and skeleton with those of other animals is well illustrated in The Natural History Museum at South Kensington, a department of the British Museum.

Thus, by recoding we mean that probably the cell of a former class of animal would be used. The basic DNA chapters of technical instructions on such features as the skeleton and body organs would be retained, but additional instructions for new features would be given.

Earth's history of life is not always one of progression. This is demon-strated by the fossil history of the graptolites, and other examples can be given. Morley Davies does so in his widely used textbook.[7]

He remarks on how the most complicated graptolites appear first and then become simpler until their extinction. This he says would appear to be in reverse to the theory of evolution. It is to be regretted that Stubblefield omits this comment in his widely-used revision of Morley Davies.[8]

Most students study the biology of the graptolites only for their exams, without also studying the geological record. They are therefore unaware that the reassembly of types according to an assumed progression is not the order shown in the rocks.

So far we have considered Coding and Recoding only in regard to living things. Prof. J. Monod and others have remarked that purpose goes back into the non-living, into matter, atoms, and sub-atomic particles. We have already spoken of their complexity.

If certain molecules and atoms attract each other in patterns as assumed by Bernal concerning the primeval soup, then we must look still further back to find God's code recorded there also. Genesis represents God speak-ing in the physical world before He created life. He not only spoke and placed His code in the world of biology, He placed His code in the realm of physics.

R. E. D. Clark says: "It is impossible to ignore the fact that biological materials are made of chemical atoms and molecules. Here, in chemistry, we are confronted by structures which do not change with time – no one imagines, for instance, that after a few thousand million years the proper-ties of water, H_2O, will have been changed by natural selection to make it better suited as a medium in which fishes can swim! So the crucial ques-tion is – do we find these apparently designed arrangements in *chemistry*, where evolution is out of the question?"[9]

Dr. Clark also says that scientists before Darwin's time claimed that they found purposeful design in chemistry. They pointed to the apparently purposeful properties of water and other substances, in evidence of this belief. Richard Owen, perhaps the greatest anatomist of the nineteenth century, thought that God had so wonderfully designed the chemical substances that, willy nilly, they would fall into the typical shapes of various orders of living things by a process akin to crystallization.

Scientists seem to be making their way back to this opinion.

Jacques Monod sees purpose already written in atomic structure. The same is implied by Prof. Sidney Fox who argues that molecules have the

[7] A. Morley Davies, *Palaeontology: Graptolites,* 2nd Edition (Thos. Murby & Co., 1956).
[8] A. Morley Davies, *An Introduction to Palaeontology.* Revised and partly rewritten by C. J. Stubblefield, 3rd Edition (Allen & Unwin, 1961).
[9] R. E. D. Clark, "Calcium Phosphate", *Crusade*, 1967.

ability to order themselves, "We need to know more about the order within physical particles, within small molecules. . . ."[10]

Even Oparin admits as much in saying "The origin of Life was not a lucky accident, but was the result of perfectly ordinary scientific laws."

If we examine the account in Genesis 1, we see that God's physical laws would also appear to be coded:

God said, "Let there be light" and there was light.

God said, "Let there be atmosphere" and the chemical properties already inherent work out their condensation (v. 6).

God said, "Let the waters be gathered into one place", and the water hemisphere was formed after condensation, and retained by the earth because the mass and gravity were already divinely calculated (v. 9).

God said, "And let the dry land appear". By some process unknown as yet by geophysics, the continents at first were formed as one land mass of silica and alumina (Sial) floating upon the ocean beds composed of silica and magnesia (Sima) (v. 9).

Also the words "create" and "make" might have their significance. In summarizing the six ages of creation, the Hebrew says that God "created to make". In other words God first had to create the raw materials before He could use and guide their formation into useful structures. The Hebrew word for "create" is "*bara*", and is the only one available to mean create out of nothing. The word is used three times; first concerning the origin of matter, the second concerning the origin of life in the waters which meets the inadequate theorizing of some "Origin of Life" biologists; and third, for the origin of man's spiritual nature, which justifies Professor Julian Huxley's requirements for a psycho-social phase, for, in Julian Huxley's opinion there were three basic phases in our universe – inorganic, organic and psycho-social.[11]

The words "make" and "form" could well describe the mechanism for carrying out the instructions of the coded DNA to the template or messengers. Movement results from energy. Did the Spirit of God create the energy for the first mitochondrion when He moved upon the face of the waters? Or was the appearance of the cell not so early in the history of this planet as some are thinking?

The opening sentence of the Bible, "In the beginning God created the heavens and the earth", confirms that creation of matter ("the heavens and the earth") was by an extracosmic source. According to this, matter is not eternal, only God is.

It would seem that these remarkable Scriptures are the record in human speech by one who had already coded in biological speech. If this possibility is rejected how are we to account for knowledge in these Scriptures which only the Creator would have at the time of writing? It should be

[10] S. Fox, "In the Beginning Life Assembled Itself", *New Scientist*, February 27, 1969.
[11] J. Huxley, BBC Reith Lectures, "Evolution", *Listener*, 1952.

remembered also that the account proceeds to record accurately prehistory between 10,000 and 3,000 years B.C.

Our inquiry would be incomplete if we left it here. The Scriptures persist that the Word which coded in the beginning became recoded in the Virgin Mary at the Incarnation by similar agencies as those at the beginning.

Since the problem for scientific investigation is that we possess only five senses through which observations can be made, we should consider the possibility that the Supernatural has communicated to us within those five senses in terms we can understand. The Scripture record claims that, "God hath spoken unto us by his Son" (Heb. 1:1). For a materialist to ignore such a communication is to prejudge the whole issue.

Fig. 20: The Human DNA Code Library. To contain all the instructions in the 46 chromosomes of the DNA code in a human being, a library of the size depicted below would be needed, according to Kendrew.

CHAPTER XVI

THE DNA CODE AND THE INCARNATION

IN THIS FINAL CHAPTER WE SHALL DRAW TOGETHER SOME OF THE varied strands of our inquiry not only as they resolve themselves into a cohesive pattern, revealing purpose in the mystery of existence, but also as they may bear upon the unique personality of Jesus Christ, whom Paul significantly called "the second Adam",[1] and who for him as for all Christians is uniquely the Son of God, "God manifest in flesh".[2]

Ultimate understanding of this mystery may well defeat our finite knowledge, but it will not do simply to beg the question, as do those who blandly declare that they do not believe in the Virgin Birth of Jesus Christ. This defeatist attitude fails to take account of our growing knowledge of the details and mechanisms of genetics, and particularly of the DNA code. Yet even as we consider, we do so in no arrogant spirit, but are conscious that we are treading on holy ground.

The prologue to the fourth Gospel is a striking application of the phraseology of Genesis 1. It becomes very much more arresting today as we are able to reconsider it in the light of our knowledge of genetic coding. "The Word" of John 1, known to the Greeks as the *Logos*, is an application of the repeated expression of Genesis, "God said". This is emphasized by other analogies which John makes. The passage is among the best known of the Bible:

> In the beginning was the Word,
>   And the Word was with God,
> And the Word was God.
>   The same was in the beginning with God.
> All things were made through him:
>   And without him was not anything made that was made.

The prologue concludes with a statement demonstrating to us that this same "Word" who Himself coded all life in the beginning, graciously allowed Himself to become coded in the DNA of the Incarnation:

> And the Word became flesh, and dwelt among us,
>   And we beheld his glory,
> The glory as of the only begotten of the Father,
>   Full of grace and truth.

[1] I Cor. 15:45, 47.
[2] I Tim. 3:16

We are not concerned with what God "could" or "could not" do by the exercise of supra-natural powers. What we note is that apparently He chooses not to go contrary to His original creation, but to use the mechanism He has already placed within that creation to bring about His purpose. He chose a human body of a woman, with its normal cellular constitution. He chose to use the normal nine months' gestation (Luke 1:40–45, 56; 2:5, 6). He appointed a doctor (Luke), to record it in Holy Scripture. The growth of Jesus Christ to physical, human maturity was also through the natural laws of God's own pre-set engineering, within the normal human experience (Luke 2:40, 51, 52).

It is Luke who tells us how the Word was coded in the DNA of the Virgin Mary:

> The angel said to her, "Do not be afraid, Mary, for you have found favour with God. And behold you will conceive in your womb and bear a son – Jesus – Son of the Most High . . .' Mary said to the angel, "How can this be, since I have no husband?"

The angel then revealed that the conception would be accomplished by two agencies, the Holy Spirit, and the Most High:

> The Holy Spirit will come upon you, and the power of the Most High will overshadow you; therefore the child to be born will be called holy, the Son of God. . . . For with God nothing will be impossible.

We take the last points first. Why did the Incarnation need two divine agents, the Holy Spirit and the Father? As John has made direct reference to the original creation we may look there for our clue. We discover that there it was the Spirit of God who was moving upon the face of the waters, presumably to organize the building-blocks of life and the self-replicating polymers. Is it therefore too much to assume that similarly at the Incarnation the Holy Spirit was active, organizing and making available the nucleic acids, with their sugar and phosphate bonds, in other words, the polymers of the DNA strand?

But the instructions to be recorded in code had to be superimposed. At creation this clearly was done by the "Word", where it is written, "And God *said*". We may also assume, therefore, that when the same Holy Spirit came upon the Virgin, He likewise assembled these nucleic acids and bonds which would be already available in the body of the Virgin. We speak with all reverence. These volumes would be assembled into the 23 chromosomes required to match the 23 in the Virgin's ovum, but would include a "Y" chromosome necessary for a male child. This would be in contrast to the formation of Eve, where the "Y" chromosome was omitted, and a female resulted.

Now comes the contrast with the original creation. Then, the "Word" evidently gave all the varied instructions into the sub-atomic particles of the physical world and into the DNA of the biological world. In the case of the Virgin, the "Most High" was the dynamic (Luke 1:35). This might be because it was "the Word" Himself who was being recorded in those nucleic acids, for He was "begotten of the Father" (John 1:14). The eventual result was that in Christ dwelt "all the fullness of the Godhead bodily" (Col. 2:9).

In this way all the fullness of the Trinity would be involved in those 23 chromosomes prepared for fusion with the ovum of the Virgin – the Holy Spirit assembling the DNA code bases, the Father sending forth the Word and the Word Himself becoming recorded upon those bases.

Thus far we have spoken of the Divine side of Christ's nature, but we should realize that the physical and spiritual, the human and divine, are not in two watertight compartments. The human side is given more fully by Luke and Matthew. Within the Virgin, the ovum to be fertilized would contain the usual 23 chromosomes. There in DNA code would be recorded already an inheritance reaching back to David, Abraham and Eve, with cellular instructions shared with the whole of mankind. Luke therefore records the genealogy of Mary back to Adam.

There are those who have asked whether the Virgin birth may not have been due to parthenogenesis. This refers to a freak case of an ovum being triggered off into separate development. This suggestion does not meet the requirements either of the Incarnation or of biology. If such a child had been born of the Virgin Mary, it could only have been a girl, for no "Y" chromosome would have been available. Also the child would have genetic material only of Mary's descent, so it would not be a true incarnation – a complete fusion of the two natures into one.[3] Also, the question of parthenogenesis appears to be ruled out by the statement in a number of places that the Virgin did conceive, but it was without any human male union. It was by the Holy Spirit, and that would be why God is referred to as the Father, and Jesus as the Son of God, and why He is stated to be born holy (Luke 1:35; Matt. 1:20, 25; John 1:14).

Our knowledge that a foetus receives a complete set of 23 chromosomes from each of its parents gives insight into the oneness of Christ's nature. Those of Divine origin and those of the Virgin would pair and fuse (in the sense of producing gametes),[4] resulting in the one personality, fully divine, fully human, without sin.

This insight into the possible mechanics of the Incarnation is a reply to those who contend that the incarnation of the Lord is scientifically impossible. It is also a help in the difficulties which some in the early

[3] J. Stafford Wright has reached similar conclusions in "The Virgin Birth as a Biological Necessity" *Faith and Thought*, Vol. 95, No. 3, 1967.

[4] Thus the Incarnate Christ would be phenotypically one, containing the genotypic gametes from alleles of the two sources at meiosis.

centuries and the middle ages had in their speculations on how two natures could become one. Modern genetics reveal that the alleles from both parents make one person at conception. The statement "That which is conceived in her is of the Holy Spirit", shows how God was the Father and the Virgin Mary the mother. Also, the fact that DNA is a code demonstrates how the speech, or "Word", of God, recorded upon the nucleic acids, would form the real genetic contribution from the Divine side. We see how that Christ was fully and truly man, and yet not two natures, but God-man, not God *and* man, thus illustrating physically what had been arrived at theologically by earlier divines.

Yet ultimately our only authoritative source for the doctrine of the Incarnation is still the revelation of God in Holy Scripture. We could not discover such things through the medium of science, but having received the revelation of God, we can note that increasing discoveries in science do show *how* it could come about, and justify the terms of reference, hitherto not fully understood by us, which God's revelation uses.

The science outlined above does not trespass upon theology, as it refers to the physical mechanism of the Incarnation, and has nothing to say concerning what part the Eternal Spirit of Jesus played in this. We certainly have not solved all the problems, for discoveries are still required to complete the picture, but the more true facts science reveals, the more they serve to increase our wonder and worship that God who is the source of all life, should Himself deign to enter that same life as a man, and do so by the very means which He Himself had brought into being.

But divine revelation can proceed into an area where science is not competent to speak. From it we learn why the Incarnation was necessary. It was among other things, in order to reveal the Father (John 14:6; 3:12, 13; Mark 9:7), and to make atonement (Mark 10:45). Because Jesus was fully man He was able fully to represent man when suffering for man's sins on the Cross. Because He was fully Divine He was able not to sin,[5] and in suffering as eternal God His sacrifice was declared completely efficacious for finite men, as well as demonstrating God's love for man. These are merely a few aspects of soteriology, but they are sufficient to justify that aspect of the Incarnation reflected in Heb. 10:5: "When Christ came into the world, he said 'Sacrifices and offerings thou hast not desired, but a body hast thou prepared me'." His was a body prepared for complete efficacy in atonement, the ultimate perfection of God's purpose in and for man.

> A second Adam to the fight
> And to the rescue came.

Within the scope of our inquiry we have considered Adam's identity.

[5] St. Augustine expressed the doctrine correctly – Christ was "able not to sin". If he had said Christ was "unable to sin" it would have implied a lack of free will and a lack of positive righteousness.

The culture, environment and geography associated with Adam act as an archaeological zone-fossil. We have demonstrated that this places Adam as a Neolithic, or at least a Proto-Neolithic man, created in Periglacial environment at the end of the last Ice-age, in what is now Turkey and Armenia. His cells probably shared a common heritage with all life on earth, but reference to his formation and the manner of Eve's origin indicate that his cells were recoded from an extra-cosmic (or supernatural) source, by the Word, or "Code", of God. This Code of God ultimately Himself inherited the cells and DNA of Adam and Eve when the Holy Spirit coded the Word at the Incarnation. Thus the Word became flesh, whom we know as Jesus Christ, Son of God, fully God, fully man, without sin.

> In Him the sons of Adam boast
> More blessings than their father lost.

GLOSSARY

Acheulean: A Lower Old Stone Age stone tool core-biface technique, which is a finer development of the earlier Abbevillian technique.

Anthropology: The Science of Man, a comprehensive term for the science of the physical, social, and cultural milieu of human beings since their appearance. It embraces distinctive inter-connected scientific fields – Physical Anthropology (human biology and genetics, fossil-man, primatology), Prehistoric Archaeology (Archaeology from Stone Ages to Iron Age), Social Anthropology (wordwide study of present primitive peoples and their legal, economic, religious, cultural and family structures).

Amino acids: (see Protein). They are the building blocks of life. By being ordered into a specific sequence they become various proteins for constructing living things.

Artifact: Anything made by human hands.

ATP and ADP: Adenosine triphosphate and Adenosine diphosphate. The energy produced by the Mitochondria to empower all processes.

Australopithecus: An early fossil hominid from Africa.

Bushmen: Members of the Bushman-Hottentot pygmy geographical population of South Africa, with a unique click language.

Catalyst: Increases the rate of a chemical reaction.

Cephalic Index: A mathematically expressed figure obtained by technical measurements of the skull.

Chalcolithic: Copper-Stone age. The transition from Stone age to Bronze age. Native copper was beaten cold before smelting was invented.

Chloroplasts: Peculiar to flora by which light is converted into energy.

Chromosome: One of the main divisions of the genetic strands, composed of many genes. Each human has forty-six chromosomes in his cells, containing hereditary information made up of DNA strands.

Codon: Groups of three letters of the DNA code which stand for letters or words in the instructions.

Cromagnon: A *Homo sapiens* western European population of tall stature, of Upper Old Stone Age, at one time classified as Caucasoid or typical "White".

Culture: The heritage of socially transmitted traits of techniques and ideologies.

Cytoplasm: The area in the cell which surrounds the nucleus.

Dental Arcades: The arch-shaped palate and jaw in man.

Diffusion: The spread of a feature of culture beyond its original area.

DNA: Deoxyribonucleic acid. Four nucleic acids are the medium upon which is recorded the triplet code. They are Adenine, Thymine, Guanine, and Cytosine, and they are usually abreviated to their initial letters: ATG and C. On these are recorded the genetic information passed from parent to offspring. These are linked together like a spiral staircase by sugar and phosphate bonds to make a chain.

Domestication: The breeding of animals under artificial conditions of living.

Dolichocephalic: Narrow, long-headed, having a cephalic index of less than 75.

Ecology: The relationship between animals and their environment or habitat.

Endogamy: Marriage within the tribe (see Exogamy).

Enzymes: The "machine tenders" who are responsible for a particular operation. They are made of protein and act as catalysts. Some enzymes have several thousand amino acids.

Eocene: A geological division early in the Tertiary or third main geological division.

Eolithic: Dawn of the Stone Age, a hypothetical period before Stone Age tools.

Eoliths: Natural-looking flint stones which are difficult to decide on whether they are artifacts.

Exogamy: Where marriages have to be contracted outside the tribe.

Extended Family: The larger group of biological relatives.

Family: A cohesive group consisting of father, mother and offspring, and other biological relatives. (Conjugal family – where father and mother are supreme. Consanguine family – where husband and wife and offspring play a secondary role, and other relatives play a functionally primary role.)

Gene: The smallest unit of heredity (see chromosome).

Glacial: Ice-age conditions.

Glaciated: Landscapes or rock remodelled by ice-erosion, i.e., U-valleys, sharp peaks and striated rocks.

Grimaldi: A *Homo sapiens* of Upper Old Stone Age, at one time classified as Negroid.

Group Marriage: The now abandoned theory that groups of males were married to groups of females.

Heidelberg: A fossil jaw discovered in Germany of a *Homo erectus* equivalent to Java and China man.

Hominids: The branch of primates leading to manlike beings as distinct from apes.

Homo: True man. *Homo erectus* – early Pleistocene man once named *Pithecanthropus*, *Homo neanderthalensis* – long-headed population of middle Pleistocene geological time, *Homo sapiens* – modern types of man.

Hottentot: See Bushman.

Ice-age: Pleistocene. Four advances of ice interspersed with warm periods. See Glaciated.

Instincts: Inherited and fundamental drives.

Joking Relationship: A relative in primitive lineal structure with whom one may joke and play tricks on – usually the Mother's Brother (or Matrilineal Uncle).

Lemur: A sub-order of the primates of Madagascar.

Magdalenian: A western European Upper Old Stone Age tool "industry", bone artifacts and cave paintings.

Maglemosian: A Proto-New Stone Age (Mesolithic or Epi-palaeolithic) culture.

Matrilineal: Group membership through descent through the mother (not through the father, see Patrilineal).

Mendelian: From Gregor Mendel, the monk who laid the foundation for an understanding of modern genetic inheritance, in 1860, but who was overlooked until the early twentieth century.

Mesocephalic: Having a cephalic index between 75 and 80, i.e. medium-headed.

Mesolithic: Middle Stone Age – a term no longer used. See Neolithic.

Microlith: Tiny flints exquisitely made by pressure-flaking, formerly associated with Mesolithic, but now of Magdalenian, Epi-palaeolithic and Neolithic eras.

Mitochondrion: The Power Stations of the cell. Within them food is converted into chemical energy used to power all cell processes.

Monomer: See polymer.

Monotheism: Belief in one God and Creator.

Mores: Modes of behaviour approved by custom.

Morphology: Study of the form and shape of living things.

Motif: Design in art.

Mousterian: Tool technique of the Middle Palaeolithic.

Natufian: Culture containing the beginnings of farming, when the Natufians still dwelt in caves or rock-shelters (from Wadi en-Natuf, Palestine).

Neanderthal: A human species which occupied all the Old World before *Homo sapiens*. Characterized by long flattish heads (dolicoplatycephalic) with prominent eye ridges, but with larger brains than *Homo sapiens*.

Neolithic: New Stone Age. Characterized by ground and polished stone tools, but since the 1960's it is seen to have a mixture of unground stone artifacts and microliths. The use of metals was not yet discovered.

Neolithic Revolution: Man's discovery of how to control his food supply by agriculture and animal husbandry, which brought about a socio-economic revolution. It began with the Proto-neolithic (once called Mesolithic).

New Stone Age: (see Neolithic).

Oligocene: The Tertiary geological epoch preceding the Miocene.

Organelle: Any discrete sub-cellular unit.

Palaeolithic: Old Stone Age. The long Pleistocene epoch culture preceding the Proto-neolithic, characterized by heavier core and flake tools for hunter gatherings.

Palaeontology: The science of fossil assessment.

Patrilineal: Group membership by descent from the father (see Matrilineal).

Peptide bond: The bond which links the amino acids in a single chain to make a protein (see Protein).

Periglacial: Conditions in the areas where glaciers terminate, such as ice-melt waters, fertile soils from moraine deposits, and restocking of plant life.

Peroxisomes: An organelle.

Phage: A virus which contains DNA but lacks ribosomes, therefore it injects its DNA instructions into a bacterium (*E. Coli*) to use its machinery to reproduce itself.

Pictograph: Conventionalized pictures for picture writing. The system preceded conventionalized hieroglyphs which referred to words.

Pleistocene: (see Quaternary).

Pluvial: Rainy. The Pleistocene glacial periods in Europe are thought to be paralleled by excessive rain in non-glaciated regions.

Polyandry: More than one husband, an extremely rare marital pattern.

Polygamy: More correctly termed "Polygyny" – more than one wife.

Polymer: A molecule formed by a chain of units termed monomers e.g., DNA molecules.

Polymorphism: Variant forms of a species.

Polypeptides: See Peptide and Protein.

Polytheism: Belief in many gods.

Potlatch: A prestige feast for giving presents to rivals amidst an orgy of destruction, practised by the Pacific Northwest-Coast Indians.

Quaternary: The fourth main Geological division co-terminous with the Pleistocene era of the Ice Ages, during which man appeared.

Primates: A classification of mammals which includes lemurs, tarsiers, monkeys, apes and hominids (including the *Homos*).

Primitive: The basic cultures of original inhabitants.

Protein: The various proteins are strings of amino acids (between 700 and 2,000 of them). A single chain is joined together by a peptide bond. A protein made of several chains is a polypeptide chain. Hair, muscle, cartilage, enzymes, blood corpuscles, antibodies, etc. are all protein.

Radio-active dating: A method of absolute measurement of age by mass spectroscopy which measures the amount of radioactivity left in the sample.

Replicate: A technical term for exact mechanical copying, especially of the genetic code.

Ribosomes: Organelles in the cell which translate the instructions of the DNA code, and manufacture the stipulated proteins.

RNA: A messenger copy of DNA which brings the instructions from the cell nucleus to the ribosomes. Three kinds of RNA in the cell are transfer RNA, ribosomal RNA, and messenger RNA.

Scrapie: This is an organism which attacks sheep and goats, but is not now considered to be a functional unit of life. Most of the evidence seems to point to it being a small protein fragment from a disrupted cell and therefore not self-replicating.

Sibling: A brother or sister.

Symbiosis: Two forms of life dependent upon each other for viability.

Sympathetic Magic: The belief that action upon a symbol will cause a similar effect upon the thing or animal symbolized.

Tort: In primitive law a wrong to be punished by the kinship group.

Varves: Series of annual sediments left by ice-melt from glaciers.

BIBLIOGRAPHY

Note: It is regretted that the author does not know of any contemporary book on Anthropology and the Bible, which has been written by a qualified anthropologist. It is hoped that *Who Was Adam?* will help to fill the gap.

Aldred, Cyril, *The Egyptians:* Ancient Peoples and Places, Gen. Ed. Dr. Glyn Daniel. Thames & Hudson, London, 2nd ed., 1962.

Albright, W. F., *New Horizons in Biblical Research,* The Whidden Lectures for 1961. OUP, London, 1966.
  From the Stone Age to Christianity. Doubleday, New York, 2nd ed., 1957.
  The Archaeology of Palestine. Penguin, London, 6th ed., 1961.

Beadle, G., *Language of Life.* Gollancz, London, 1967.

Beattie, John, *Other Cultures.* Cohen & West, London, 1964.

Beer, Sir Gavin de, *Genetics and Prehistory.* The Rede Lecture, CUP, 1965.

Bernal, J. D., *The Origin of Life.* Weidenfeld & Nicolson, London, 1967.

Braidwood, R. J., *Prehistoric Men.* Chicago Natural History Museum and The Oriental Institute, Univ. of Chicago, 1957.
  The Near East and the Foundation for Civilization. Condon Lectures, Oregon State System of Higher Education, Eugene, Oregon, Third Printing, 1962.

Brothwell, D., and Higgs, E., *Science in Archaeology.* Thames and Hudson, London, 2nd. ed., 1969.

Brothwell, D. R. *The People of Mount Carmel.* "Proc. Prehist. Soc." 27:155, 1961.

Camping, H. "J. Amer. Scient. Aff.", Sept. 1970. p. 98.

Carter, Cedric O., *Human Heredity.* Penguin, London, 1962.

Chardin, Pierre Teilhard de, *The Phenomenon of Man.* Fontana Books, London, 2nd Imp., 1965.

Chedd, Graham, *What is Life?* BBC TV series produced by Edward Goldwyn. BBC Publications, 1968.

Childe, Gordon, *The Prehistory of European Society,* Penguin, London, 1958.

Clark, Grahame, *Archaeology and Society.* Methuen, London, 1960.
  World Prehistory (An Outline). CUP, London, 2nd ed., 1962.

Clark, Robert E. D., *The Christian Stake in Science,* The Paternoster Press, Exeter, 1967
  Darwin: Before and After. The Paternoster Press, Exeter, 1966.
  The Universe: Plan or Accident? The Paternoster Press, Exeter, 3rd ed., 1961.

Cole, Sonia, *Neolithic Revolution.* British Museum, 1964.

Dewar, D., *Man: A Special Creation.* W. H. Houldershaw, Southend-on-Sea, 1946.

Daniel, Glyn, *The Megalith Builders of Western Europe.* Penguin, London, 1963.

Davies, L. Merson, *The Bible and Modern Science.* Constable, Edinburgh, 4th ed., 1953.

Dye, David L., *Faith and the Physical World:* A Comprehensive View. The Paternoster Press, Exeter, 1966.

Evans-Pritchard, E. E., *Nuer Religion.* OUP, 1967.
  Theories of Primitive Religion. OUP, 1965.

Finn, A. H., *The Author of the Pentateuch.* Goodman, Taunton.

Filip, Jan, *Celtic Civilization and its Heritage*. New Horizons. Academy of Sciences and Artia, Prague, 1962.

Firth, Raymond, *Human Types: An Introduction to Social Anthropology*. Mentor, New York, 5th imp., 1963.

Forde, C. Daryll, *Habitat, Economy and Society*. Methuen, London, 1964.
African Worlds. OUP, London, 4th ed., 1963.

Ford, E. B., *Mendelism and Evolution*. Methuen, London, 7th ed., 1960.

Frankfurth, H., *Birth of Civilization*. Doubleday, New York, 1956.

Gamow, G., *The Creation of the Universe*. Mentor, New York, 1952.

Harrison, R. J., *Man the Peculiar Animal*. Penguin, London, 1958.

Jacobs and Stern, *General Anthropology*. Constable, London, 2nd ed., 1959.

Keiller, Alexander, *Windmill Hill and Avebury*. Clover Press, London, 1959.

Kitchen, K. A., *Ancient Orient and Old Testament*. Tyndale Press, London, 1966.

Kidner, Derek, *Genesis*. Tyndale Press, London, 1967.

Kenyon, K., *Digging up Jericho*. London, 1957. (See also reports in Palestine Exploration Quarterly, 1952–8).

Laming, Annette, *Lascaux Paintings and Engravings*. Penguin, London, 1959.

Leakey, L. S. B., and V. M. Goodall, *Unveiling Man's Origins*. Methuen, 1969.

Leakey, L. S. B. *Adam's Ancestors*, 4th ed., London, 1953.

Le Gros Clark, W. E., *The Fossil Evidence for Human Evolution*. Univ. of Chicago Press, 2nd ed., 1964.
History of the Primates. British Museum, 7th ed., 1960.
The Antecedents of Man. Univ. Press, Edinburgh, 1959.

Levine, R. P., *Genetics*. Holt, Rinehart & Winston, 1962.

Lloyd, Seton, *Mounds of the Near East*, Edin. Univ. Press, 1958.

Lovell, Sir A. C. B., *The Individual and the Universe*. OUP, London, 1958.

Mellaart, J., *Catal Hüyük*. Thames & Hudson, London, 1967.
A Neolithic City in Turkey, "Scientific American", 1964.
Anatolia Before c. 4000 BC. CUP, London, 1964.

Martin, W. J., *Stylistic Criteria and the Analysis of the Pentateuch*. Tyndale Press, London, 1955.

Mendenhall, G. E., *Law and Covenant in Israel and the Ancient Near East*. "Bible Archaeologist", 1955.

McEvedy, C., *The Penguin Atlas of Ancient History*. Penguin, London, 1967.

Mixter, R. L., *Evolution and Christian Thought Today*. A Symposium by Members of the American Scientific Affiliation. The Paternoster Press, Exeter, 1959.

National Geographic Soc., *Everyday Life in Ancient Times*. Ed., G. Grosvenor, Washington, D.C., 1951.

Nilsson, Heribert, *Synthetische Artbildung (Synthetic Speciation*: includes 100-page synopsis in English). Gleerup, Lund, Sweden, 1954.

O'Connell, P., *Science of Today and the Problem of Genesis*. Radio Replies, Minnesota, 1959.

Orr, J., *Problem of the Old Testament*. Nisbet, London, 1907.

Ordnance Survey, *Ancient Britain*. Southampton, 2nd ed., 1964.

Oakley and Muir-Wood, *Succession of Life Through Geological Time*. British Museum, 5th ed., 1962.

Oakley, K. P., *Man the Tool-Maker*. British Museum, 5th ed., 1961.

Oppenheim, A. Leo, *Letters from Mesopotamia*. Chicago Press, 1967.

Pearce, E. K. Victor, *Origin of Man*. Falcon, London, 1967.

    Proto-neolithic Adam and Recent Anthropology. "J. Amer. Scient. Aff." 23:4 pp. 130–9, Dec. 1971.

    "Darwin", "Evolution" in *The New International Dictionary of the Christian Church* (The Paternoster Press, Exeter, 1974).

    Flood and Archaeology, "Faith and Thought", 101 (1974) 228; 102 (1975) 19.

    Biblical Flood: Evidence from Egypt, ibid., 103 (1976) 126.

    Essay review of C. Renfrew, *Before Civilization*, ibid., 101 (1974) 163.

    Letters from Mesopotamia. Oppenheim Review in "Man". Royal Anthrop. Inst. London, Dec. 1968.

Piggott, Stuart, *Neolithic and Bronze Age in East Europe*. "Antiquity", vol. 34, 1960.

    Rise of Civilization. Thames & Hudson, 1964.

    Neolithic Cultures of the British Isles. UP, London, 1954.

Pospisil, Leopold, *Kapauku Papuans of West New Guinea*. Holt, Rinehart & Winston, New York, 1963.

Radcliffe-Brown, A. R., *Structure and Function in Primitive Society*. Cohen and West, London, 4th imp., 1961.

Radcliffe-Brown and Daryll Forde, *African Systems of Kinship and Marriage*. OUP, London, 1962.

Ramm, Bernard, *The Christian View of Science and Scripture*. The Paternoster Press, Exeter, 1955.

Romer, A. S., *Man and the Vertebrates: 2*. Pelican, London, 1962.

Sherlock, R. L., *A Guide to the Geological Column*. HMSO, London, 2nd ed., 1957.

Spanner, D. C., *Creation and Evolution*. Falcon, London, 1965.

Solecki, R. S., *Prehistory in Shanidar Valley, Northern Irak*. "Science", vol. 139, pp. 179–93, 1963.

Thompson, J. A., *Ancient Near Eastern Treaties and the Old Testament*. Tyndale, London, 1969.

Towers, Bernard, and Lewis, J., *Naked Ape or Homo Sapiens?* Garnstone Press, London, 1969.

Ucko and Dimbleby, *The Domestication and Exploitation of Plants and Animals*, Duckworth, London, 1969.

Wissler, C., *The Cereals and Civilization*. American Museum of Natural Hist., NY, 1946.

Wood, E. S., *Collins Field Guide to Archaeology in Britain*. Collins, revised ed., 1967.

Watts, W. W., *Geology for Beginners*. Macmillan, London, 1953.

Wiseman, D. J., *Illustrations from Biblical Archaeology*. Tyndale, 1958.

Zwemer, S. M., *Origin of Religion*. Marshall, Morgan & Scott, London, 1935.

INDEX

COMMENTS AND OPINIONS
ON "WHO WAS ADAM?"

Prebendary E. K. Victor Pearce asks WHO WAS ADAM? and with the use of his considerable anthropological knowledge and expertise finds an answer convincingly more in harmony with 'Genesis' than would have been thought possible, even in the circles of the extreme right, a few years ago. Before this wealth of well-substantiated argument many strongly held opinions may appear to be mere preconceptions of the left and many details of criticism dissolve in the deeply religious conclusion. Many readers will appreciate the side swipes at the more bogus type of Teilhardism.

Expository Times

No part of the Bible has been more discussed than its early chapters. Since the rest of the Bible seems in many ways to be an unfolding of its start, these chapters are vastly more important than their length might seem to warrant. Yet after the interminable discussions of the past, what is there left to be said?

A great deal, thinks our author. But whether we are disposed to listen to him or not will depend on how we think the Bible should be interpreted. If we believe it can be understood by reference to itself alone we shall think lightly of this book. If, however, we think that interpretation is sometimes impossible save in the light of knowledge which was not available at the time the Bible was written, we may feel most indebted to Canon Pearce.

Faith and Thought

This book deals with exciting discoveries in the fields of anthropology and biology, and the unity and continuity of all life as seen in the cellular and sub-cellular organisations of our bodies.

Mowbray's Journal

"I am astonished at the breadth and depth of scientific knowledge in the book."

The Most Rev. George P. Dwyer, D.D., Ph.D.

... readable, thought-provoking and concise. It would make a good basis for a study group of scientists and theologians.

Theological Students' Fellowship Bulletin

"Victor Pearce moves with a sure touch through prehistory, archaeology; also genetics and DNA coding so far as is relevant to the origin and development of all living things, including Adam and Eve, and, in a most worthwhile chapter, to the unique birth of Jesus Christ."

J. Stafford Wright
(Spectrum)